Shake Hands With A Bum

SHAKE HANDS WITH A BUM

Phil McGrath

Caliban Books

First published 1986
by Caliban Books
17 South Hill Park Gardens
Hampstead, London NW3

ISBN 0 904573 95 8

Typeset by Witwell Limited, Liverpool.

Printed and bound in Great Britain by
Wheaton & Co. Ltd., Exeter, Devon

CONTENTS

In memory of my parents
and to Sharpie. With love
from my heart and I.

INTRODUCTION

I first met Phil McGrath ten years ago when he came to the Yorkshire Television studios in Leeds. He had brought the manuscript of "Shake Hands with a Bum" to Austin Mitchell, now a Labour MP, but then a television presenter.

Phil appeared to be every inch the retired boxer. Small, red-haired and wiry, his craggy face had a defiant look about it, as if its owner would be prepared to fight the whole world if necessary. His manuscript looked as dog-eared and ill-used by life as Phil himself.

Yet, both Austin and I were astonished when we read it. "Shake Hands with a Bum" is raw and painful, and extraordinarily honest. Take the directness of his description of how at the height of his success Phil drinks with a down and out, the kind of man he will all too soon become himself.

> "He looks my way slyly with watering eyes. I can feel the room take on a silence. The chatter has changed to murmurs. The old man's bony hand trembles, holding his half glass of beer. We stare at each other for a moment, and then I hand him the double brandy. He grasps the glass with greedy hands, a grin comes from his quavery mouth. He drinks away his sadness."

Unlike conventional boxing writing such as "I am the

greatest" (Muhammed Ali) or even "Raging Bull" (Jake La Motta), this book is a portrait of a loser, not a winner. Phil McGrath never knew great fame as a boxer, largely because of the inherent character defects that he so self-laceratingly describes. His wild, tearaway style earned him a big reputation as a crowd-pleaser, and fights with many top boxers such as Maurice Cullen and Vic Andretti, but, like his approach to life in general, it lacked the patience and foresight to bring long-term success. His career could have been more fruitful if he and his advisors had planned his life as a boxer rather than taking any fight, however ill-matched, that promised to pay a few pounds.

It was typical that, as the book describes so well, when his chance to stand in for Terry Spinks and fight the world's number one lightweight contender at Wembley finally came, he was serving a period of suspension imposed by the British Boxing Board of Control. Phil was completely out of training and working as a dustman in Halifax at the time, but the inevitable defeat was marked by his customary courage under heavy punishment.

Yet, however tellingly "Shake Hands with a Bum" captures the atmospheric world of scrap-metal dealers who double as boxing managers, and third-rate boxing halls in Northern England, the book is about so much more than boxing.

As its centre, the narrative has a family relationship that is portrayed with an emotional intensity that matches David Storey's "This Sporting Life". Phil's mother is loyal and patient, but the key is Phil's relationship with a self-destructive and cruel father whom he worshipped.

This relationship is, in McGrath's words, "the heart

that makes the story beat". He describes his father with obvious love and complete honesty. The picture, memorably, is of a magnetic but bitter little man with a contempt for life. Towards the end he seems determined on self-destruction through drink. It's this man who encourages his son's boxing career, yet rarely lets the boy get close to him, whose praise the boy desperately needs. Outside the ring, Phil feels inadequate compared to his father, "only half a man". (It is drawn against a backdrop of urban poverty, with boxing one of the only escape routes from the slums, as Phil tries to "make a somebody from a nobody".)

Just before he dies, Phil's father Charlie McGrath is admitted to a sanatorium.

> "I was shocked when I first went, he was old and feeble in his forties: he couldn't have weighed more than 6 stone. I could not believe that this very same man once knelt down to spar with me! Only his eyes were the same, forever watchful, staring out of their sunken sockets, always that cruel stare . . . but never a hint of pain came into those eyes, and it was this that stabbed my mother, making her feel so helpless. If a blind man is standing in the middle of the road, how do you help him to safety if he refuses help?"

Charlie McGrath inspired in his son a combination of worship and fear. After his father's death, with almost Shakespearian inevitability, Phil too began to boost his fragile self-confidence with drink. It brings about the end of a promising boxing career and of his marriage. Even when successful, the seeds of self-destruction are there. After a victory in 1960 he says, "I felt like a king among beggars with my own house, my beautiful wife, the gold ring on my finger, eighty pounds in my wallet. But I was a restless king, hankering after what I lost on the way up."

The book is full of dramatic scenes, some grim and bitter, others comic and amusing, but always described with a remarkable absence of self-pity. Phil's schoolboy boxing experiences, the accidental killing of the family cat, a street party, and the agonising build-up to the big fight with world-contender Rafuie King at Wembley are all drawn with clarity and strength. All this is beautifully etched in against a backdrop of urban poverty, with boxing one of the few escape routes from the slums as Phil tries to "make a somebody from a nobody." Yet, Charlie McGrath's slow, sudden death through alcoholism and the strange mixture of love and hate that he inspired in his son dominate the book.

The second time I met Phil was in Northallerton Prison. He had been sent there for a short spell following his usual offence of assaulting someone whilst under the influence of drink. We talked about his troubles, and his writing.

He showed me the original manuscripts of "Shake Hands with a Bum". The entire book had been written clandestinely in prison into small prison notebooks with a stubby pencil. Since then scarcely a word has been changed. For Phil McGrath there is no revision process, no polishing of words, it's written straight from the heart. He told me that, like George Orwell, he believed that "autobiography is only to be trusted when it reveals something disgraceful."

Phil's been out of trouble for eight years now. He lives in Yorkshire and is unemployed; he's trying to write. For someone with so little education, "Shake Hands with a Bum" is a remarkable achievement, it is unique book, where honesty and pain cry out from every page.

John Willis

CHAPTER 1

IMPRISONMENT

It was a misty September night, the drizzle had silently been falling on the cold hard pavement. My left shoe was beginning to squelch, it had a hole the size of a halfcrown in the sole. I had already walked past the black stone building countless times. This time I was going in. A shiver passed through my body. Oh God! I feel so damned cold and lonely. I absently touched my chin with my right hand, and felt the stubby growth of my beard. Suddenly it began to itch, I clawed it vigorously and then without thinking I scratched my crutch. A feeling of tiredness and weariness enveloped me. I felt like a small boy who wanted to tell his mother all the wrongs he had done. What is this demon drink that makes me terrified to wake up for the fear of the wrong he has done. What, Dear God! can make a man so low as to sleep in his own filth. Please tell me God, tell me the secret how some men are strong, and others like me are pathetic and weak. At first it seemed that I was the strong and they were the 'Oh! so bloody weak', self-righteous creatures, but look at me now:- note how I'm cowering, trembling, and apprehensive, wondering if I should confess to the terrible wrong I have done. But I must. I will. It is the only thing I have left to restore a little self-dignity.

The forbidding entrance of the Police Station loomed in front of me like a nightmarish dream. I pushed open the door and walked in. Trembling legs took me to the desk. The sergeant sat astride a stool talking into the telephone.

He looked up and glanced my way, covering the speaker with his hand, and with a bored expression on his face motioned me with his finger to hold on a minute. I thought how easy it would be to turn and walk out, but I stood still enjoying the warmth of the room. No desire had I to run, it was just as if I had been nailed to the floor. Nothing seemed to matter any more. I felt so calm it did not seem possible.

The sergeant's voice broke into my thoughts, words came from his rubbery lips, "Yes Phil, what can I do for you?" The bored expression remained on his face as I answered "Nothing, sergeant, there's nothing you can do for me." He gave me his 'here we go again' look, but I went on, wanting so much to shake him out of his dutiful manner. "It was me that did the snatch on the old dear." Suddenly the bored expression became bored no more. "Would you mind repeating that?" he asked, as if he were asking me to close the door. I told him once more. He stood up with solemn reverence and motioned me to go through into the office, opening the swing doors which led to a passage. I glided through in V.I.P. treatment. The door to the cell-like room stood uninvitingly open. A table and a chair were its only furniture. The sergeant told me to sit down and said that he would send someone in to see me. Relieved that the first part was now over I waited with amazing coolness. The key turned in the lock again and I was confronted by a C.I.D. man and a policewoman. He turned to the policewoman with exaggerated noncholance, "Joan, tell the sergeant to make some tea. You would like some tea wouldn't you Phil?" he asked automatically. I nodded. The policewoman left the room. "Now then Phil, I've got these statements for you to sign," he said pleasantly, as if he were asking me to sign a passport to go on my holidays. I suppose in a way I was. The policewoman came back with steaming cups of tea, and placing them on the table asked "How many sugars Phil?" "One please" I said, not taking my eyes off the detective. She then went and stood by the door. The C.I.D. man sat with pen in hand, waiting for me to commence the sordid details. I told him everything, signing the statement with relief. Placing his Parker pen back in his pocket he asked "How the hell did you ever get into this state Phil?"

It would be too long a story to tell you Mr. C.I.D. man. Maybe there is no answer to that question. Perhaps I was just born to be a loser, perhaps we can't all go around wearing badges on our blazers sipping our f..... bitter lemons, because I really feel to a certain degree that one must be false, just like you are Mr. C.I.D. You have to put on this act because it is part of your job, but maybe tonight you'll take your mask off and tell your wife how you conned Phil McGrath into making a statement, or maybe you forgot how to take the mask off.

"I don't know" I mumbled, "I just want some sleep." "Certainly Phil" he said, gathering up the statements from the table, "I'll get the jailer to bring you some blankets," and with that he left the room. "How do you feel?" asked the policewoman. "Oh alright" I replied. I really did too. The jailer came and led me down the passage, passing each cell door. I heard a cough and thought to myself at least there is one other poor bastard in here with me. The fat jailer gave me two grubby blankets and said "Alright Phil, this will do", pointing to an open cell. I threw the blankets on the wooden bed board, jumping swiftly in, in full attire. I lay there glad that it was all over, but loneliness was not far away. I was so cold.

Thoughts passed through my mind with fleeting swiftness, childhood thoughts of days so long ago, remembering the time when I was picked to represent

Halifax Schoolboys at football. Yes, I can remember it so very clearly now. There were four of us, but I was the only one from a 'B' class. The Headmaster called each in turn upon the platform in front of the assembled boys and girls. I was the last to be called out, my stomach twittering with excitement. The Headmaster, a gentleman, shook me firmly by the hand and congratulated me. I walked back to my place as proud as could be. All the boys were ribbing me and I was really enjoying myself. The Headmaster had come down from the platform and left the hall. One of the teachers had taken his place, trembling with rage, as he stood on the platform waiting for the noisy chatter to subside. I turned round to some of the boys and said "Sh! Quiet". At that moment the teacher shouted "Right you, McGrath, come out here"; I stood, amazed, not believing that I was actually being reprimanded. I staggered to the front of the hall, pushing past the still noisy kids. "Alright McGrath, just because you think you can play football it doesn't mean that you haven't to do as you are told." Pointing with his finger, he said "You will kneel in front of the school." It is funny why I should think of that now, maybe it's because I spoilt everything good I ever did, but really I don't think that teacher called me out because I was talking, there were twenty or thirty others talking as well. I think that maybe it was because he was the first to see that I could never be a person for people to look up to, no examples could I set. He was probably the first to sense the seed of the rebel in me. I pulled the blankets down from my chin. I must remind the jailer to let me have a shave. I feel so bloody scruffy.

* * * * *

Forgive me if I don't go into court procedure, allow me

the luxury of omitting the full details. I had done a terrible wrong and was at the mercy of the court. My feelings were neither of sadness nor relief, I just felt an empty overpowering disgust for the thing I had done. At the time I thought I had paid my debt to society - but do people let you off the hook so easily? In some ways I was at a disadvantage. I was once a respected citizen of Halifax, but while one commands respect, it does not necessarily mean that one is liked. There is always a certain amount of jealousy for a successful person. I call these jealous people 'Ringside Critics', they are near enough the ring to give vent to their feelings, but too far away to get involved in what is going on. By having a good view of the boxers he feels he has the right to make cutting remarks because after all he has the best seat. What he fails to admit, or conveniently forgets to remind himself is that he has not got the courage to go into the ring himself and fight, so he does the next best thing and gets as near to the fight as he feels safe and criticises any false move the boxer may make, whether it is the man's fault or not. This idea never enters his head.

Let us say, for instance, a man called Joe Soap is in trouble for the third time that month. My Ringside Critic sitting in a big armchair, in his nice little semi-detached house, sipping a cup of tea, nibbling his biscuits, reads from the evening paper to his wife, "I see old Joe Soap has done his wife again, the silly devil". The thought dismissed, then feeling in a better mood turns to the sports page and reads all about Halifax Town's latest defeat. What he fails to realise or even think about is:- why is old Joe Soap always beating his wife; what makes him act like a man with no reason or sense? The main point is, the reader feels in a better mood because he is not in this poor condition himself. He is comfortable, while Joe Soap is down and out and far enough away not to hurt him. The more he criticises the better he feels. All he has to do is follow the crowd and he can't get hurt. Then again, he can never be an individualist because he has not got the courage to stand out and really say how he feels to Joe Soap's face.

Anyway, like Joe Soap, I was in prison. I refuse to go into details of prison life, except to say how one dreads the deadly routine of it. It revolves around you day in and day out, never ceasing. If you have never been in prison, please try to imagine yourself in your coffin, except that you are alive, eating and sleeping and abusing yourself. When you get a letter you are really happy - if you don't then you are depressed. You are living in a world of the living dead, so when you are released it is like being reborn. Now I feel it is time for me to be reincarnated and start my story from the beginning, or as near as possible as one can remember certain things.

CHAPTER 2

MY THOUGHTS OF CHILDHOOD

"Ivy, how do you expect me to get the results down with all this bloody noise?" Dad has his paper and pencil at the ready for the football results. This was Saturday night in the McGrath house. He did not stop there. "Get those two little buggers upstairs," the "two little buggers" being my twin brothers Tony and Stephen. My mother, a small, plump woman just under five feet tall, stared across at dad with a look that by rights should have killed him, picked up Stephen in her arms and carted him through the door that led up to the bedroom. I jumped up from the chair, grabbed Tony and followed my mother out of the room.

In the bedroom mam was putting Stephen in the pram. She was crying. She turned her head as she heard me come in. "Thanks love" she said as she came and took Tony out of my arms, then she went and nestled him in the twin pram with Stephen. She went over to my bed and sat down heavily, she looked round at the distempered walls, taking in every bugmark where my father had been trying to burn them out with a candle. Suddenly she got up from the bed and went over to the pram and looked down at Tony and Stephen. I knew the thoughts that were passing through her head:- What kind of life is it where I have to bring my babies up in a bug-infested, one-up, one-down middin'. Her thoughts tumbled into words: "Philip love, do you know why we are in this dirty hovel? We are here because he is drinking himself to death. God, Philip, don't you ever touch the stuff!" I thought to myself, what is this drink that makes my mam go on in this way? I once had a taste of the stuff and it was awful. My mum went on:- "If it is not his drink, it's his bloody horses, or his sodding sport, when he comes in everyone has to stop breathing for him."

I knew this had been building up inside her ever since he had got the sack. He had had a nice steady job bill-postering, but the boss had caught my dad and his mate 'pissed' in the middle of town.

As I was thinking, I could hear the man with the results on the wireless:- "Huddersfield Town 2 - Bolton Wanderers 1; Preston North End 1 - Wolverhampton Wanderers 1." My mam was still chuntering to herself. "He won't do anything around the house. Maybe it's just as well, he is bloody useless anyway. If he tried to hammer a nail in the wall he'd miss it." I knew what was coming now- it invariably did when she was on the warpath - "You can't go out for a quiet drink without him wanting to fight the whole pub. All he ever gave me was babies and this twin pram." My mam was really proud of that pram. Dad had had a good win on the horses and she had got hold of some of the money before he could spend it; mind you, that was not my dad's version when telling his pals!

My dad was a small bloke about five feet-four tall. Unlike my mam, he was wiry and even though he drank like a fish he did not have any fat on his body. Most people don't give a damn about being small, but my dad felt different. He thought that because he was small he had to prove himself, whereas a big man could go through life on a "physical free ticket". Let us say that two men have gone for a job, both men are exactly equal in their skills one of the men is six foot tall, the other is five foot one. The foreman studies the situation and he plays safe by picking the biggest man. So it's obvious that physical appearance does count, just ask a woman who her dream man is and invariably she will plumb for a tall man, but a little man with a squint in one eye could be twice as good a bloke! But my dad made the mistake of trying to fight "big tree"; he usually came unstuck - but he learned a lot even by losing. My father did not talk a lot, but when he did you somehow felt priveleged that he was speaking to you.

★ ★ ★ ★ ★

Dad was in a way a symbol of Woolshops, the area of Halifax in which we lived. He worked when he could, drank as often as he could and gave my mam as little as he could get away with. Yet this man was the one whom my mother loved and I part-loved and part-feared. This was the man that men respected. He did not go round corners when he answered a question, he was straight to the point. A man's man. He loved my mother in his own special way, but this love was deep and did not often show, but it seemed all the more special when it did.

So these were the ingredients to the early years of my life, a rather strict and stern father and a soft-hearted and loving mother.

CHAPTER 3

A SEARCH FOR EXTRA

Everyone remembers his first fight. It is like one's first love, more often than not you lose, but always you look back with a little sadness and affection.

I was nine years of age when I made my debut as a bare fisted John L. Sullivan. My weight was trimmed down to a tidy four-and-a half stone, he had an advantage of three inches in height and his father owned the "Ring O' Bells" pub along the street. My dad was barred from there because he had told the Landlady to cover her head up. Anyway, me and this boy measured one another up, and then he jabbed a straight left into my face. I tasted my own blood. "I'll kill you, you bastard," I shouted, but it was me that was getting killed. He was punching me all round the bloody street. Just as quickly as it had started it had finished. I fell to the ground and lay there moaning. "Well have you had enough?" he shouted. "Yes" I said. I staggered to my feet, covering my face with my hands and walked off towards Nelson Street. He shouted after me, "Next time you'll get worse, short arse" - I did not stop to dispute him. Dad was sitting on the steps of our house, Topsy, our cat, lay on the step below him. Dad was bent over, stroking her. He looked up as I tried to get past him into the house. "What's up with you?" he said as he noticed my face, "How did you get that thick lip?" I told him I was running and had tripped over. He said "Who are you trying to bloody well kid?" You have had a crack in the mouth. Who gave it yer?" "That kid whose dad owns the "Ring O' Bells", I answered. Dad was smiling. "You pick 'em big, lad," he said. "I'll beat him when I get bigger, dad," I said. My dad laughed and replied "Well he'll get bigger too, you daft bugger," still smiling as he said it. I thought to myself, why can't he always be like this. He bent his head to stroke the cat. His black curly hair dropped forward, then he said "You will never be a big person, Philip, and the only way you will ever beat a big bloke is by having something extra, and the only way to get that extra is to work for it. I will take you to watch them training at the 'Saddle' boxing club next Sunday, and if you like what you see I'll let you be a member." "Wow, thanks dad" I said. "There," my dad said, "I don't think you should say anything to your mam yet." "No dad," I said and ran back on the street to tell my mate, Terry O'Rourke.

The Saddle Boxing Club was a large room above a pub. How can I ever begin to explain the feeling that passed through me as I walked up the stairs that led into the room? Have you ever walked into a room and seen a woman standing there and thought with all certainty it is she I want more than anything else in the world, and you knew without speaking to her that she felt that way too?

I can see it now as if it were only yesterday. The men sat around that large room, guzzling their pints. It seemed that they all came from from Woolshops. Men skipping, others sparring and shadow boxing, the smell of sweaty bodies.

We walked into all this activity, dad and me. Men shouted "How yer going on Charlie? 'That your young 'un?" Dad smiled at each of them. I felt an uneasy, scary feeling in my stomach as I looked in the full atmosphere of the crowded room. I tried not to miss anything, it excited me so much. "Please dad, can I join?" But he wasn't there.

He was standing talking to a man dressed in a vest and pumps. Then my dad turned and shouted "Come over here, Philip." When I walked over to him the other one said "Well he's only a little bugger, Charlie, but we'll see what we can do with him." My dad said "O.K. Edgar, but if he causes any trouble, just throw him out."

This, then, was the start. It was a thing to which I gave all my time and attention. Some boys can play with a Meccano Set or a train set for hours, but this boxing thing was something that I really wanted to strive at, to be good at, not only good, the best.

Boxing became an obsession with me. I trained at the club and when I wasn't at the club I trained with my pal, Terry O'Rourke at home.

Dad was really hitting the bottle, but I was getting a little more attention than I had ever had before. There was a kind of perverted obsession when boxing was mentioned; it was as if he was willing me on, implanting a cruel attitude inside me. You may think is it not cruel to instill such things into a small boy, but is it not also cruel to give your child everything, to cuddle and pamper him? Dad was not an expert on boxing, but he knew what life down Woolshops was all about. He would say "If you are prepared to throw a punch you must be prepared to take one". Then he would say "Don't take one when you can duck one." Was not this the attitude of people down Woolshops?

So this was how it was Edgar trained me in the fundamentals of boxing, and the old common sense philosophy coming from dad.

Life down Woolshops still took its day to day existance. Men still got drunk and beat their wives, mothers still prayed for the day when they would be free from the place, people still gave us cold stares, teachers would still sit us at the back of the class for fear the other kids would collect some of our nits. But we kids did not care about anything in those days. In most cases we were healthier than our tormentors - and we most certainly did not cry as easily. What did it matter if we ran through the streets with our shaved heads? Why should we care if we wore the same clothes everyday? Or about being late home for our tea? - all we had to do was dive into a jar of jam or spread lard on our bread.

How are kids to know the way of grown-ups? The shot-up snobbery around them - we were deaf to the glib remarks that were directed our way. What do we care, we kids from Woolshops are alive aren't we? We can run, fight, kick and climb walls better than most kids. Is it not just a matter of luck where one's "spermatoza conceives?" Nothing really touches you when you are young. How one wishes that you could go back in time when nothing matters. But one grows older. You become more sensitive to your surroundings. At the age of ten I was sitting up and beginning to look at things with a small child's shrewdness; then you realise the nature of the things around you, the tears in your mother's eyes, the bad moods of your father, the poverty that surrounds you. Then, and only then, do you realise that Woolshops is pure HELL. It seemed that all the women folk were drawn close together because of the fear that their men would come home, drunk, from the pubs and ill-use them.

How I have lain in my bed and listened to them coming home drunk. Men shouting and women screaming, my mam's voice saying "Come in Charlie, don't start again." I can hear the foul language, everybody talking at once. I hear dad swearing at someone, my legs start trembling. I am sweating. They are outside the house. "Come in Charlie!" shouts my mother. Screams echo in the street, my legs jingle an uncontrollable dance. Oh mammy! I'm so scared please hurry and be quick and come in. It's so dark in the bedroom, mam shouldn't put the blanket up to the window, it does not show any light. Dad said I was not to get out of bed except when I want a pee. That's because I once saw a ghost and I ripped the blanket from the window. A right big copper came and broke the window downstairs to see what the matter was. He was a nice copper with a red face and blue eyes. He sat me on his knee and jogged me up and down. I kept laughing at him and he said "What yer laughing at Shamus?" I told him that there was some hair sticking out of his nose. He started laughing and gave me sixpence. I really did like that copper, even if he did call me 'Shamus'.

Its gone so quiet on the street. I hear a door bang shut and mam chattering away. I hope she doesn't make dad mad. I feel a lot better now.

When I grow bigger I'm going to be a famous boxer, with a big house and a car and rosy apples on the trees, and people will say that's Philip McGrath the boxer and they will ask me for my autograph. Yes that's what I'm going to be - a famous boxer. Dad's overcoat was slipping from the bed. But I still like it on me, it makes me feel safe when the ghosties come out.

★ ★ ★ ★ ★

Little did I know what, at that time, my life would turn out like. However, this is no way to write my story, hinting at things to come. I must keep to the thoughts and dreams of my childhood. I must bite into the inner core of life to find out just where the badness or the weakness bore it's first fruit. So, like the small boy who longs for the days to pass so that he can change from a boy to man, I must walk down the street of childhood memories peeping into every crevice, looking in every alley way, delving into the small boy of long ago. Where did we go wrong, you and I? You with your determination and never ending battle for respect, what of me, small boy, can you help me to find out the inner feelings of my downfall? Will you help me to peep into the alleyways of yesteryears, or will you too shun me, little boy, you, who has always wanted respect, you who has always wanted your big house and garden, you so confident and so dedicated. Is it possible that you will turn against me too? No! that cannot be, for you are me, and I am you, and if I am a bum you are one as well. You are the core of the apple, the bullets for the gun; without you I would never have been what I am. Please do not think that I am blaming you, small boy, but why, oh! why? this obsession for respectability, and I lost you the respect you once had, you will see whether those friendly slaps were actually knives, stabbing in your back.

Surely my little one, neither of us has really used the common sense we were given. Would dad not have said "A man keeps his respectability because he does the right thing all the time." When you were successful he told what a great boy you were, and what a credit to the town you were. He shook your hand and bought you a drink, he introduced you to his friends. But alas, when I came on the scene, he left you bewildered and shaken. You may say do not blame them for our downfalls, and I most certainly am not, but do not belittle yourself too much, you remember you are the only person that got yourself out of Woolshops. What I would like to ask you is - is it so important to have to lose your respectability or did it mean so much to you? Is it worth the effort to be one of them? But this is your part of the story and you are the heart that makes me beat.

Nelson Street was just above the gasworks. Terry O'Brien and myself would run home from school, collect our coke bags and run down to the gasworks in next-to-no-time. We would nearly always beat the other kids as we lived so near, but very soon all the other kids from Woolshops would congregate in queues round the gas ovens, pushing, fighting and swearing at each other. By this time, Terry and I would already have handed over our bags and fourpences. We would nonchalantly swing them over our shoulders and away we would walk on the road, glad that we lived so near. "See you later, Terry." "O.K. Philip," Terry shouted, running into his house across our small narrow street. Mam was putting the wet clothes through the wringer, her black hair falling over her forehead. "Oh Philip, I want you to run to the shop and get me three candles, the mantle has gone again" she said wiping her hands on her apron. "Oh bloody hell!" I mumbled to myself. "What did you say?" said mam. "Nowt." She went on "Well you'd better not, your dad will be home in another hour."

"I have put my name down for the boxing championships at school." Her big brown eyes glared at me. "Don't talk to me about your boxing Philip, you know I don't like it and I never will, nothing ever came of people that fight." "But I'm not fighting, I'm boxing," I protested. "Go on, get on with you," she said, giving me a friendly push off the step. Poor old mam, I thought, she would not hurt a fly - but dad would be pleased about the championships.

I had already had my tea when dad came home. Mam was washing the twins before putting them to bed. "How's it gone today Charlie?" she said, picking up Tony and powdering his bottom. "Oh alright" dad said, putting a spud in his mouth. He picked the local paper up and automatically turned to the sports page. I watched him fully scan the page, and then stop at the 'Stop Press' for the racing results. Mam was putting our Stephen's sleeping shirt on. "Did you have a bet on today Charlie?" she said slyly, looking at his back, then glancing over at me. "What?" he said, then remembering what she had asked, said "No I didn't have a bet today. I haven't any money, you know that, Ivy." He said it as if he really meant it, she looked at his back and smiled. That smile said, you are a liar Charlie, but I still love you. As if sensing that my mam would continue on this very delicate subject, he pushed his plate away and got up from the table. He gave her a sly look and said, "I right enjoyed the tea, Ivy." I sat watching the two of them, sensing a dog fight. Entranced by both of their personalities: mam grown crafty over the years of living with dad, dad forever watchful and wary from the inquisitiveness of mam's relentless attacks.

"Dad," I interrupted. I saw the relief on dad's face, and ignoring mam he said "Let's have a sit down". "Dad," I began again, "I have put my name down for the schoolboy championships". I saw mam out of the corner of my eye give me a dirty look and going to the sink bang the talcum powder on the shelf. Dad looked at her and smiled. "When are they son?" he asked. "Three weeks, up at the army barracks hall" I said. "We will have to get you in tip-top condition" he asserted, glancing at my mother. "Ivy, we will have to buy him some shorts." Mam turned round on dad and said "He's getting no shorts out of my money." I replied kindly to her, "It doesn't matter, mam, I can get some from school." Dad whirled round on me and said "What you mean is pinch them"; I just smiled a small boy smile. Dad shouted: "Well, I am not bloody well smiling." My smile vanished. "I'll have no pinching in this house" he stated. I knew for a fact that dad used to get the coal on the knock. He jumped up from the chair and said "I'll get your fancy shorts, but remember it's the man in them that counts."

He went towards the sink and stripped to the waist, then, pouring hot water from the pan into the basin, said "Remember, Philip, if he is a bigger boy, not to stay in one place too long, otherwise he will measure off with his left, so remember what Edgar keeps telling you, keep moving whatever you do, duck, weave, but keep moving." I really had got him going. "Get the gloves out," he said, "I'll give you a few rounds". Then dropping to his knees he waited for the gloves.

One hour later and still we were punching each other silly. I felt so proud being there with him. Mam was sitting on the step talking to Mary and the twins were upstairs asleep, and here I was with my dad, just us two alone. Dad had caught me some good'uns to the face and my nose was bleeding, but that didn't bother me. I would show my dad how tough I was. A spot on dad's bald patch was bleeding. "Have you had enough?" dad said touching his forehead with his right glove. "No, have you?" I said cheekily. Dad grinned, and all the shoutings and beatings that he had given me had vanished as quickly as the grin had come. "Well we will call it a draw" dad said, chewing on the lace of his glove. Later I sat in the tin bath by the fire, dad swilled water on my head, sleeves rolled up. Silence except for the splashing of soap water.

Dad put my nightshirt on and told me to say goodnight to mam. "Goodnight, my love," she said and grabbed hold of me, she kissed me on the cheek, I blushed and ran upstairs. I heard my mother laughing. I jumped into bed, I was so tired and very soon I was asleep. I must have slept for five hours. I opened my eyes and saw dad getting into bed. Mam was bent over the pram fussing over Tony and

Stephen. "My little babies, aren't they grand, Charlie?" "Yes" said dad, "Wait till they wake up and then you will see. Come on Ivy, get into bed." "Wait a minute," she snapped. She came over to the little bed, I blinked my eyes shut, I pretended to be asleep. She tucked the blankets in. I felt her face so very close to mine, she kissed me on the forehead, a finger ran down my nose. "You have bruised his nose, Charlie," and then I heard her move away. "I don't like him getting hurt," she said. I heard dad mumble "If he only gets a bruised nose he won't do bad. I'll tell you this" he went on, "he's a game little bugger, and he does not know when he is licked." I could see that mam had turned her back on dad and was sleeping.

CHAPTER 4

SCHOOL

Our school was no more than a mile from Woolshops. Terry, my mate, who lived across the street from me would call round at ten-to-nine every schoolday morning. Then off we would go, chewing on our bread. Tugging and pulling each other, laughing and giggling, but mates. "Philip, why are you wearing those wellington boots, they must be at least two sizes too big for you," he said, smiling. "You can hardly lift your feet off the ground" he went on. "Because my dad said it would make me feel lighter, and when I fight on Friday night I will be able to move round the ring like a blue-arsed fly. That's what my dad said," I answered. "They'll all laugh at you in school" Terry said, so I replied to him "Dad said I have not to give a bugger". Then Terry said "Your dad's nuts." "What do you mean by that" I retorted, taking an aggressive step towards him. "I don't mean that way," Terry blustered. "Which way do you mean?" I asked, looking puzzled. "I heard my mam and dad talking and my mam said he was always causing trouble when he was drunk, and dad said that he pissed out of the window coming back from Wembley last year. Remember, Philip, when your dad and mine went down London for the Rugby Cup Final?" "Yes I remember," I said, looking at him sullenly.

We walked towards the steps leading to the schoolyard. I could hear the bell just start to ring. "Come on Terry, I'll race you to the assembly hall", I said as I clambered awkwardly in my wellington boots up the steps. "Wait for me, you rotten sod" Terry shouted, but I was away running into the cloakroom and then into the hall. Everyone was standing in their places. I felt the eyes follow me as I dragged the wellingtons across the floor. The headmaster shouted everyone to attention and morning prayers began. This was the routine every morning. One solid hour of prayer chanting. I glanced at the door just as Terry came in, his eyes darting anxiously round the hall. One of the teachers gave him a piercing look. I took in his cheeky face, his protruding ears, the hole in his sock and the shirt tail sticking out of his pants. I smiled to myself, and as if knowing I was smiling at him, he looked me in the eyes and gave me that cheeky grin, that only he could do. I winked at him and there was our bond.

I looked at the kids singing hymns; one of the girls looked at me. I blushed and turned away, then I thought to myself - fancy dad pissing out of the window coming back from London.

CHAPTER 5

THE FIGHT

The barracks hall was full to the brim that cold Friday night. All the parents were there in full force as well as kid brothers and sisters of the boxers.

I walked nervously into the dressing room. Everyone was talking excitedly. A boy came over to where I stood "What they call you?" he asked, looking me up and down as if I were a prize cow. I told him and away he walked shaking his head. A tall, thin boy stood in the middle of the room, waving a programme. "Anyone here called McGrath?" he shouted, his eyes taking in all the room. "Yes over here," I whispered, my throat suddenly failing me. He came over, looking at his programme, "You Philip McGrath?" I nodded, my heart thumping fifty to the dozen. "Well you're fighting me" he said, seeming to like what he saw. I watched him strutt away. "Philip", my dad was saying, emptying my pumps and shorts on the table. I awoke from my trance feeling a comfortable warmth within me. "How do yer feel?" he asked, putting white laces in my pumps. "Alright," I replied unenthusiastically."You don't sound so bloody confident" he snapped disgustedly. "Who yer fighting?"

"That tall boy over there" I said pointing to where the lad was sitting. Dad looked over and took in the bony knees and the tall thin frame. "Christ, I have seen more meat on a butchers apron", he laughed. I knew he was just trying to cheer me up. "Oh, by the way" he went on, fishing a shilling out of his waistcoat pocket, "Edgar said I was to give you this now, and if you put him away I will buy you some fish and chips." I smiled. "Listen lad, he is a damn sight more scared than you are." "How do yer know dad?" "Because I do know, that's why," he said. "I have been watching him staring across at you."

Sure enough his eyes never left mine. "Listen lad, when that bell goes I want you to go straight across the ring and put him out of his misery." "But Mr. Green, our teacher, told us we have to feel him out the first round, dad." "Balls to your Mr. Green. Go at him from the first bell. Right, let's have them wellingtons off" he said, snatching at my left boot. Everyone was beginning to change. I stripped down to my vest and shorts. "Right, on with your pumps" dad said, putting my jacket over my shoulders. I was still shivering. "Oh there you are Philip," Mr. Green shouted from the other side of the room. He came striding towards us, a red sash in his hand. "Well, well, Philip, I am sure you will not let us down. Here you are" he said giving me the red sash. "Just slip it round your waist. Oh, you must be Mr. McGrath," he said, squinting over his glasses. Dad nodded. "Well I am very pleased to make your acquaintance", Mr. Green went on, enthusiastically shaking dad's hand. "Oh, by the way Philip, remember to shake your opponent's gloves before and after the fight. Yes, that's the main thing, to be a good sportsman." Dad was looking at him disgustedly. Mr. Green turned and walked quickly out of the room. "How do you feel in those pumps?" dad asked, placing the wellingtons under the table. "Light as a feather, dad" I said happily, thinking of our little secret. "Well I am going to watch the other fights Philip, so for God's sake don't take too long with him, the pubs will be closed soon."

I walked towards the ring, the butterflies fluttering

wildly in my stomach. Mr. Green was in my corner. "Ah, good show there McGrath" he said, the towel flapping in his hand. "Give him the works, Philip." I looked into the sea of waving faces, noticing Terry's waving hand. "Oh yes, I see your friend O'Brien is with us. Jolly good show", Mr. Green said. I had a sudden urge to run away back home to mam, how did I get here? Mr. Green was fussing around me, feeling the gloves, playing with my sash. Panic came upon me. Strongly, my eyes searched the hall for him, wanting so much the incentive that only he could give. Then I saw him, crouching down the side of my corner. He stood up abruptly, looking me directly in the eyes. Calmness came back to me like fresh smelling air. I turned away from his gaze, walking now so confidently into the centre of the ring, looking at the boy with all the hate I could muster and feel within myself, and I saw, like dad he was scared.

I went back to the corner waiting impatiently for the bell to sound. The hall was hushed then I heard my dad's voice just as plain as if he were the only one in the hall. "O.K. Philip, let's get home for those fish and chips." Clang the bell tolled out for the first round. People were still laughing at dad's remark, but even that was forgotten when he jabbed a left into my face. A deep anger flared inside my belly. I tore into him. The punches going from all angles. His mouth was agape, his nose trickling blood, but I could no more stop punching than my dad could pack the booze in - and why should I? Was this not my outlet? Was this not the key to respectability? Was this boy only getting his just reward? For all the hatred I had of Woolshops, if it means butterflies in the belly, blood on the boxing gloves, are they not worth such small aggravations to be at last somebody?

The referee was tugging at my arm, someone grabbed me and led me back to my corner. Mr. Green was chattering on, but I couldn't understand. Then slowly my fury subsided, leaving me a feeling of disgust, like someone caught pooping in class, never realising that you had let one off. "You really must learn to control your temper, McGrath" Mr. Green said shooting words out like a Tommy gun from his mouth. "I will tell him what he must do", dad shouted from the ringside, in a menacing tone. The announcer was speaking:- "Referee has stopped the fight in the first round - Red the winner." Dad and Mr. Green were taking me back to the dressing room. Mr. Green said "I was only telling him what to do. He really must learn to control his temper." "Yes that's fair enough," dad said, "but it was the way you said it that I didn't like. I don't wish you any disrespect, but your attitude and mine are totally different. You tell your boy to wish his opponent the Best of British Luck, I tell my boy to stare 'im out and say nowt. My boy was wrong for losing his temper, but not for the same reasons you have. Your reasons are that he could get disqualified and thereby he would be letting the school down. My reasons are that one day he will meet a better, bigger boy who will take advantage of his weakness and then he will be on a hiding to nowt. The way I'm tellimg him is diplomatically. By telling him your way you will kill off the killer instinct he has undoubtedly got", he said, looking down at me. "You don't learn boxing from a book, Mr. Green, you have got to have it there" he went on jabbing his finger in his chest. "And a boy without a killer instinct is like a snake with no bite."

Mr. Green looked shocked at dad's outburst. "Well," he stammered, "Eh. Eh. Well done Philip" and shook dad's hand again. "It's the Yorkshire Finals next, Mr. McGrath, I hope to see you there. I believe they are at Thurnsco, Rotherham," he said, his face reddening. "Well, goodbye,

goodbye", putting his overcoat on and striding out of the room. Dad was smiling. "Right Philip, on with your jumper and coat" he said, placing my pumps and shorts in the carrier bag. I was feeling tremendously happy. Was it really me in that ring tonight?

Outside, dad gave me another shilling. "Get yerself some fish and chips. I won't be long. I'm going for a pint." Skipping across the road, I ran down into the town centre but my wellington boots slowed me down to a dragging walk. I was so excited I just couldn't wait to get home.

★ ★ ★ ★ ★

I had already got to the fringe of Woolshops, passing the gloomy houses, noticing men standing in groups talking and smoking, the womenfolk shouting for their children to come in for bed, where they should have been long ago. A small boy was urinating in the street, his pants round his ankles, his face as black as coal. Two small girls were slurring their mothers' shoes along the pavement. I passed close by them, doing my best to avoid their cheeky glances, yet somehow compelled to look at them. I took in lipstick plastering tight-lipped mouths, the silly headscarves and beads wrapped round their necks. They giggled and whispered something to each other. I felt my blood rise and cheeks go crimson, gripping my carrier bag tightly, I hurried down the streets. Coming out on Nelson Street I saw mam sitting in dad's chair. In her hand she had one of dad's shirts. "I have won, mam" I said, raising my voice excitedly. She looked up from sewing a button on the cuff. Topsy was playfully pawing at her legs. "Get away" she said, pushing the cat hurridly away. "So you won," she went on, her face breaking into a smile. "Well I should think you have, what with all those bashings you have took off that stupid dad of yours. By the way, where is he?" her eyes suddenly saddening. "Oh, he went for a drink - mam, dad gave me some money for fish and chips and Edgar gave a . . ." - but mam interrupted, "Alright, get to the fish shop. I'll cut you some bread."

"My, oh my," the fat lady behind the counter remarked, splashing raw fish into the pan. "You look so pleased with yourself Philip." "Yes" I said excitedly "I won my fight at the barracks and dad's treating me to fish and chips". "Oh, he is, is he? Well we will treat you as well" she said, throwing a good helping of scraps onto the paper.

Mam was buttering bread. "Now sit yourself down, love, and lets get them wellingtons off you." She grabbed my right foot, struggling and jerking till finally it came off, sending mam falling back into the chair. We were both laughing. "What a daft bugger your dad is" she said, tears of laughter coming into her eyes.

CHAPTER 6

REQUIEM FOR A CAT

Topsy our cat was dad's pride and joy. He fed her all the titbits from his plate. He was forever boasting about Topsy's prowess. He would say "Yes, she has killed two rats and twenty-two mice." Even the street had a high regard for Topsy. The children would stroke her and pat her gently on her sleek black back . However, Topsy was getting old and sometimes it showed. It seemed that dad fussed over her all the more. He watched her carefully, noting if she ate her food with the same enjoyment, and where we all put our feet down if Topsy were around. Mam once put a yellow ribbon round the cat's neck and told the neighbours that dad had bought it for her on her birthday. The neighbours, knowing Charlie McGrath was far from a sentimental person took delight in this bit of news, severely punishing him for his affections towards the cat. So in time it became a settled joke in the street. "How is Topsy's cough? They have some good throat lozenges at the corner shop." They would all taunt my dad. It made him go white with rage. Mam would laugh till the tears ran down her face. She would say, "Oh, Charlie, they are only having a bit of fun" and then she would burst into fits of laughter once again. "I don't care, Ivy, they are not having it at my expense" he would moan, and he would look into her smiling face, her cute little nose and big brown eyes, and who knows what thoughts would pass through his head. What, but only the most gentle of thoughts could enter into his head when looking at my mother. Then he would smile and grab hold of her and rub his stubbly growth on his chin into her face. I would watch and feel so happy, because happiness is a form of disease, it is contagious. This is what I came into contact with when I was close to my mother. It was as if my mother was saying to my father "Why do you take life so seriously, we live and we die, Charlie, and in between we must be happy, for what is life without happiness? Happiness is found in your heart, not in the material things of life."

But, alas, I am getting away from part of my story that I personally dread. I now have to report a death. The death of Topsy, our cat, or should I say my dad's cat, it does not really matter any more.

I have now to confess that I was the cause of that death, so in actual fact, I am a murderer. I will leave the judgement to you, but whatever decision at which you arrive, please bear in mind that I have already been punished. I will now proceed with the depressing details.

Topsy had a habit that when the oven was on a low fire, she would jump into the oven and go to sleep. Now the oven is a very old fashioned one. It has a door and sides made from cast iron. Mam would blacklead the door every two or three weeks. The oven itself is built into the fireplace with the actual fire around it. It is the fire being built up which causes the oven to get hot, consequently, when the fire is low, the oven is just warm.

The Sunday dinner was finished. Dad went upstairs for his afternoon nap, mam put the dishes in the sink to soak in hot water and went outside to where the twins slept soundly in their pram. I got a comic and sat on dad's chair, reading it. Soon I got up. I went to the door and saw mam up at the end of the street talking to a friend. My pal, Terry, was walking up the street, he spotted me and shouted "Are you coming out?" "No" I said. "I'll get the gloves and then we can have a few rounds in the house, dad's upstairs in bed, so we won't have to make much noise." We went into the house and moved the sofa to the back of the room. "Right, put the gloves on, Terry," I said as I threw him a pair. He snatched the gloves and put them on, tucking the laces inside. We started at a mad pace, punches were going all over the place. We went on for several minutes, then Terry caught me a good one. Crack. I stumbled back and felt a jarring in my back as I fell against the open oven door. I turned and banged it shut, making sure it was latched firmly, and then tore back into the attack on Terry. We were both having a good old set-to when mam walked in the door and snapped "Right you two, out." "Ah mam" I said. "Out" she said "or I'll shout your dad up." We both slunk out of the house.

Mam glanced at the fire and proceeded to put coal on to build it up. She then went to the sink and washed the dishes.

I can only surmise what happened in those two hours while I was out, but there is no doubt that the cat my dad loved, Topsy, was in the oven.

Dad came down from the bedroom feeling refreshed from his Sunday sleep. There was also no doubt about who was the first to find Topsy, because mam saw him cry for the first and only time. He cried over the hedgehog-like corpse of Topsy, but this was a thing I was not to know until the fatal moment.

Terry and I had wandered off after mam had thrown us out of the house. I could hear my mam's soprano voice halfway up Woolshops. "Phil-eep" she sang out. I turned and looked into Terry's face as if asking for confirmation.

"Phil-eep" she sang again. "That's my mam" I said. "No it aint" Terry said. It rang out once again. "Yes, that's my mam;" "I wonder what she wants you for?" said Terry, putting his right forefinger to the side of his nose and blowing. "I dunno. It's too early for tea" I replied, feeling uneasy. Terry said "Alright, I'll wait for you" as he kicked a stone in the road. I ran down the street and looked back to see if Terry was still waiting. He was, sat on the edge of the pavement, dropping dirt slowly out of his hands down the drain grate. He looked up as if he sensed that I was watching him. "Hurry up" he snapped. I nodded and jerked my head round and ran home.

Mam was stood on the steps, her face was chalk white. I stopped. "Yes". There was something wrong. My uneasiness increased. "Come in Philip, your dad wants to have a word with you" she said gravely. I walked through into the house. Crack... I felt a blow at the side of my ear. I spun across the room, banging into the far wall, but dad was on to me in next to no time. Crunch... my nose was spouting blood. "Charlie, for goodness sake, you said you would just talk to him", I heard my mother scream. Blood was gushing down my shirt. "That's gone far enough" my mam said, as my dad had one last kick at me. "You rotten bastard" mam shouted. Dad spun round on her. His face was white with anger. He took a step towards her. "Don't you ever call me that again" he said. I sat by the side of the wall, sobbing quietly, the slaver running down my chin, intermingling with the blood on my shirt. I stared vaguely round the room, like a blind man seeing for the first time in years of darkness, and yet seeing things so clearly, noting even small objects, dad's shaving pot with his brush sticking out. The mirror on the sink door with the crack where mam had thrown the bottle of vinegar at dad.

My eyes rested on the table. What can that be on the tin tray. It looks like a prickled bush. No, wait a minute, it's a hedgehog. Yes that's what it is. Topsy must have caught it outside and brought it in. My eyes searched the room for Topsy. Where are you, Topsy, I want to give you a cuddle for bringing it in. I looked across at the hedgehog and suddenly I knew without doubt that this thing was Topsy. The tears streamed down my face. "Oh, mam, what have I done, Mam?" I spluttered. "It's alright, love" she said, wiping my face with a damp cloth. "He won't touch you again, he has gone out." I said "Mam, that is our Topsy" I sobbed pointing to the tray. "Yes luv, but it's no good upsetting yourself now, she's gone and that's that" she said. "Besides she was getting old anyway." I could hear the neighbours talking outside, but nobody interfered with family squabbles down Woolshops.

The door was flung open and I looked up into the face of my dad. I moved closer to my mam for protection, and pulling her arms around me she said "It's alright luv." Dad picked the tray up and walked towards the door with his back towards us. He said "I want him in bed by the time I have buried Topsy." "But he hasn't had any tea, Charlie," my mam said. "I don't give a damn, I want him in bed by the time I get back" he said, as he went out of the door, closing it. Was not that the door of my childhood closing as well, for something happened that bleak Sunday afternoon so long ago? Did I not see life in its true perspective when I saw that door shut? I could never hate a man like I hated my father that Sunday, yet I could never respect a man as much as I respected my father, so why the hate, and even more so, why the respect? Was my hatred for the beating he gave me, or did it stem from the humiliation of the beating? Did I not vow that he or anyone would never humiliate me again? What of the respect? Why should you respect a man who punches and kicks you? Why should you respect such a man? What can I say? - because he is my father?

No, that's not good enough my conscience says. Well what can I say? I ask. You can at least try to tell the truth, my conscious says. Alright, I will endeavour to tell the truth. My first reason is because he married my mother, therefore I respect his shrewdness. Do I get a point? Yes, but it is a cheeky one. Well, my next reason is that he does not paint you a flowery picture of life. He tells you and also shows you that it is cruel, and he also shows you how to be prepared for it.

So, my conscience says, by treating you cruelly, he is, in fact, preparing you for it. No, I object, let me finish, please. You cannot call my dad cruel when he sobbed over a dead cat and beat his son for being the cause of it, for I was indirectly its murderer, so I must be punished. By punishing me he is being fair. But I suggest to you that it was not that he beat me that was cruel, it was the way he actually did it that was cruel. That is what bothers you? Speak conscience and let me hear your views. I am tired. I want to sleep. I am exhausted. Yes, we are both tired. We shall sleep.

My mother was shaking me awake. "Come on, love, you are going to be late for school. Your dad's already gone to work, besides, Terry is downstairs waiting for you," she said, looking sympathetically at my face. I ran my tongue around my dry, cracked lips, and tasted the dried blood on my top lip. So dad had not forgiven me. I pushed the blankets away from me, thinking how much I hated him, I took my nightshirt off and reached for my corduroy trousers and shirt from the bottom of the bed. Downstairs, Terry was sitting at the table, gulping down tea. His eyes darted towards me as I came into the room. Mam was asking Terry if he would like some more bread. He looked at her sheepishly and said "No thanks, Mrs. McGrath," but mam persisted in giving him the slice of drip-bread.

"Morning Philip," Terry said, as if he were living in the house permanently. "Terry was telling me that he is in a class above you", said mam, smiling at me, as if to ask if that was right. "Yes", I murmured, looking maddeningly at Terry, who was fidgeting and looking down at the table. "You had better frame yourself, or you will end up like your dad, taking any job you can get" mam said.

At the mention of my dad's name I turned round and gave her an angry stare, but as if not noticing, she went on, "Well it's true. In a few years you will be at work, and you must start to take an interest in something. There are more things in life than sport. I want you to get a decent job when you leave school. One that you will be interested and happy in." I listened with a bored expression on my face, then, as if knowing that whatever she said would make no difference to me, "You had both better be going." I rushed my tea down and looked at my mam's face. "See you tonight, mam" I stated. "Alright love," she said, "Hurry home and I will have something nice for you:" I knew she was thinking about the beating I took yesterday.

CHAPTER 7

THE LOCKED DOOR

There was still a week to go before the Yorkshire Championships, but still my dad had not said a word to me since that day three weeks ago when Topsy died. He had already gone to work in the mornings when I got up, and I was already in bed by the time he came home at night, via the pub. I would ask my mam if he had said anything, but she would shake her head and reply that he had hardly even said anything to her.

I was still training at the boxing club, but it did not seem the same without dad's interest. It was as if I had lost the incentive, so, if I had lost the incentive, it seems as if I just wanted to impress him. What would it mean if I won my Yorkshire badge in comparison with a few words of praise from dad? So I carried on skipping and sparring, but even that was just automatic when the incentive wasn't there. Even so, it was better than sitting at school not being able to do your lessons and showing little inclination or interest in attempting them.

I somehow got the feeling that this was a crucial step in my life. A feeling I had was telling me that I had to win this fight. I felt an uneasy, insecure feeling that I would end up like dad. I had a craving to be somebody important, and yet begging my dad to give me the key which would open the door onto this other world, which only he had. Yes, even at that very youthful age, I swear to you that I possessed this terrible dread of insecurity. This was the only thing that kept me skipping and sparring with Edgar when all the others had gone home. This was the thing that kept me from having a sly smoke in the school lavatory, not the fear of being caught. That lingering dread of insecurity. So it went on, from day to day, this yearning for dad's guidance, and with only a week to go, not a word had he uttered to me. I felt like I had lost the incentive like the soldier who waits for his commanding officer to shout the order for battle, for it is his officer, and him alone that he will listen to, yet having that uneasy feeling that he was dead, and that soldier had a terrible dread that he was on his own, but still hoping and praying that he would appear to inspire him. Pray do not think that I lacked confidence in my own ability, with all modesty, I certainly did have confidence, but it was the deeper, psychological type of confidence that I so desperately sought.

Mr. Green and Edgar were too nice a nature to possess this sort of psychological warfare, they were happy and contented in their conditions. In Mr. Green's case it was the honour of taking part in the Championships alone that contented him. In Edgar's case, it was good enough for him to be training boys for it, that satisfied him.

They too were happy in their day-to-day lives. They had what they wanted, a comfortable existence, they were in no way ambitious, they were perfectly contented in their uncomplicated lives. They had small vices, like most people, but their's did not expand into addictive weaknesses - whereas dad had an attitude best described as all or nothing, and in his case it turned out to be nothing. Maybe at one time he had the attitude and determination to succeed, I really don't know, because dad has never been a person to delve into the inner history of his life. One thing I did know was that he had an uncanny insight, sifting into your every thought; - yet his life was full of complications and complexes, often violent moods thrown in. Men still admired him for the way he spoke, making what they thought a difficult predicament come out as a minor detail. It was as if he were unravelling all the complex moods and weaknesses. He stored away all these things in his head and marched them out in regimental order; he knew where it was going, yet was always leaving something behind to antagonise himself with when he was drunk. But why? Oh why, the drink, dad?, you most certainly could have been somebody, I know. Just like other men. It is as if life were so meaningless. Surely, surely this is not fate. I can remember my dad telling my mam one night, that he was born to drink. I remember the way he said it. He did not whine like a child, nor shout it in one of his outbursts, he said it just as a statement of fact. I remember my mam's voice answering him. "You are talking rubbish, Charlie", and there was not a falter as she spoke my dad's name. Dad was one never to speak rubbish. Speak out of turn, speak glibly, yes, but never rubbish, and this was something my mam knew very well.

I thought of mam, a simple person until roused. What was it she saw in this strange man, or was she fated around this man for better or worse, what was this hold my dad had on her? Oh she lost her temper with dad, but soon after she seemed to love him twice as much. I don't think I will ever find the answer to that question. I don't think even my mother knew herself.

Mr. Green had asked me if my dad was going to Thurnsco. I told him that I would let him know. I had somehow gathered that Mr. Green had changed his opinion of dad, or at least taken a more realistic view of dad's opinions and attitudes. Whatever the reason, he genuinely wanted dad to be there. He had said that they would be running a coach to Thurnsco and that I had to let him know by the morning. I went home that night, determined to wait up for dad and ask him outright whether or not he was going.

Mam and I were sitting by the fire when he came in, his face grimy with grease from work. Mam glanced quickly at the alarm clock, and looking at dad, noticing the cruel stare which dared her to start, she said "supper in the oven" - emphasising the word "supper". She then got up and went upstairs to bed. I sat there trembling, keeping my eyes focussed on an object on the shelf. He stripped to the waist; I stole a sly glance at the matt of black hair on his chest. I heard the sound of gulping and splashing as he doused himself in the cold water, then I heard his voice as if for the first time. "What are you doing up?" he said, as he dried himself with the worn out towel. Even from where I sat he reeked of drink, but his voice remained calm. I stuttered my answer, "Mr. Green wwwants to know ar-are you going to Thurnsco t-t-to the boxing Championships." He said: "Yes. Tell your Mr. Green that I am going to bloody Thurnsco. Tell him that I hope you get a worse hiding than I gave you." Then taking a look at the oven, said "Now get out of my sight."

I lay in bed sobbing. I knew that mam was awake, but I could no more stop sobbing than bring our Topsy back. "Hush, my love, go to sleep", I heard my mam's voice, soft and tranquil. "He hates me, mam" I sobbed into my pillow. "No my love," she said, "He loves you, he loves each one of us ." "But he just", I hiccoughed, "he just told me that he hopes I get beat." Mam replied, "But you won't, will you, my love?" I said a little excitedly, "No, I won't you see mam, I won't." Mam replied "Well go to sleep, or you will wake the twins, and you show that dad of yours." I was sure she was smiling as she said it.

CHAPTER 8

DAD LOSES OUT

The coach was full by the time dad and myself climbed in. Mr. Green looked nervously at his watch as we got in and said "Oh good show, Mr. McGrath," patting me on the head. "Please sit at the front with me. Well that's everybody" he said with a sigh of relief. "You can go now, driver," he said. I nodded a greeting to a couple of boys I knew and sat across from dad and Mr. Green. "Put your bag up there, Philip" Mr. Green told me, as he pointed to the rack above my head. Then he turned to my dad and said "How are you, Mr. McGrath? I'm so glad you could come. It's a beastly night to hold the tournament." The bus started off, and Mr. Green asked my dad "Well is he fit?", as if my dad should know. Dad looked at me, his eyes like two steel ball-bearings, and said "Well are you fit?" He just ignored Mr. Green. "Yes, I am fit" I replied, looking defiantly back at him.

Mr. Green, as if sensing the friction between us, asked dad where he worked. Dad told him. "I work at an engineering firm" and Mr. Green said "Oh, really," as if he had a job in the secret service. Then he asked "What are you - a fitter?" "No" dad said, "I'm a . . .-" "I knew it", Mr. Green interupted, "I knew it, you are a turner." But dad said "No, I'm a bloody labourer", in a disgusted tone of voice. Mr. Green looked sadly at dad as if saying you poor man. Dad grinned and said, "Why, do I look like a turner, Mr. Green?" The grin illuminated into a broad smile, changing the steel ball-bearings that were his cyes into small cut diamonds. Yet just as quickly as it came, the smile vanished, leaving the steely eyes to look out watchfully. "Oh no, Mr. McGrath. May I speak frankly?" Dad nodded, and Mr. Green went on, "You er, give me the impression that you have a quick brain. When you spoke at the barracks I pondered on what you had said. I'm afraid I do not agree with your attitude, but you certainly gave me food for thought;" he went on, "but like you said, your world and mine are totally different, or should I say our attitudes," he stated with a gentle smile. "No, Mr. Green, I did not say 'worlds' at the barracks, but let us keep to 'worlds', because they are totally different and therefore if our worlds are so far apart, which we both agree on, then we each must have a different concept of it." Dad went on, "You are a damn nice bloke, Mr. Green, you try to see the good side in everyone, I would even go so far as to say that you push out all the unpleasant evils from your sub-conscious, but they are all around us, and we in our world must act accordingly. Now you ask me what I was, a fitter or a turner, and may I thank you for the compliment, once again the good came out of your sub-conscious. I'm a bloody labourer, and a bloody poor one at that, and when I'm not looking at the clock at work I'm in the pub. You said you thought I had a quick brain. That's not a brain, that's insight. Insight into our world, and our world is your world, only you wear the falsities of life, and we," he smiled, "have been stripped of them. I'm sorry Mr. Green, please have your turn and speak."

I looked across at dad and thought that I had never seen him like this, so gentle and considerate. "In actual fact" said Mr. Green, "you are a non-conformist." Dad grinned and said "What have I to conform to? To a one-up-one-down where we all sleep in the same room; to a rent man who sticks the rate up every time we catch a bug?"

"But you realise that you are leading to self-destruction" Mr. Green said. Dad smiled, the diamonds came out once more. "Surely I don't have to conform to that", he said, but Mr. Green went on, "Oh yes, Mr. McGrath, you do. You most certainly do. You have a responsibility to your family," he said, looking at me, "even if you have not had the good things in life, your fault or not, you most certainly owe it to them."

"But you say", dad interupted, "it is as if it was as easy as picking apples of a tree." Mr. Green went on,"I don't mean the material things. I mean the will to live, the eagerness to survive." "Survive to what?" Dad spoke loudly. "I think our roles have done an about-turn," said Mr. Green. "You have said that Philip has the killer instinct, and by implanting your attitude, I have no doubt that he can go far. Your attitude is to fight to the death, butt him with your head, heel him with your glove, as long as you do not get caught, just as long as you are there for your arm to be raised at the end of the fight. But what of your fight, Mr. McGrath, where are you when you should be training? You are in the pub knocking the pints back. What is it when you have to keep looking at the clock, is the fight too hard, and where has your killer instinct gone Mr. McGrath, or your stamina to survive? Should you not be practicing what you preach?" Dad looked at Mr. Green, his eyes aflame, then suddenly he was smiling. "Do you know something," he said, "Mr. Green, I like you." Mr. Green replied "I like you too, Mr. McGrath." "Call me Charlie" dad said. Mr. Green said "Rightho, my name is Cecil, but my friends call me Ces."

The bus splashed into Thurnsco. The rain, relentless in its bid to empty the clouds, poured from the skies. You could sense the uneasy atmosphere that had descended on the bus. Mr. Green stood up, and facing the back of the bus, spoke in a kindly voice. "Alright, boys, I think it is time to wish each and every one of you the best of luck, and if some of you do not win, I want you to remember that it is not the winning, but it's the taking part that means most." He looked nervously down at dad, remembering his approach to attitudes, but dad was listening with a new respect for Mr. Green. He coughed and went on: "So good luck, boys. Good Luck. Right, up you get". We jumped off the bus, some splashing in puddles, some laughing nervously, but each one of us pretending, watchful for the slightest sign that would betray the fear we all felt. Thereby boosting each others egos, we marched into the hall like soldiers going into battle, excited by our own fear – the Tommy Atkins of the ring. That feeling that we were scared to be scared, rushing to the lavatory to relieve ourselves, then we would all go back into the hall to stare fascinated at the battle ground. Our battleground. The boxing ring, with the sheening white canvas, and the ropes contrasting vividly with the red and green padded corner posts.

I stared at the bright red bucket with the bottle of water and sponge, and back at the canvas. I thought of blood splashing on the white canvas, like the rain outside. I suddenly thought I was glad that I had brought my wellingtons. I looked round for my dad, and there he was, my commanding officer, looking round the empty hall, his eyes missing nothing. Please dad, help me, give me the courage to win the fight. Don't desert me when I need you most. Dad came across to where I stood, next to the ring. I knew he wouldn't desert me. "Well," he said, " it's a big-sized ring, you will be able to run away with no bother." Did I hear him right? "Because that's what you are, bloody well yellow. So yellow that you have to put a cat in the oven", he spat out. "Well" he went on, "I won't be satisfied till you get the beating I know you will get" he said as he walked away. Tears came to my eyes, I felt so helpless, but as quick as they came the tears subsided. I thought the no-good bastard, I'll show the drunken swine. He comes home and gives my mother a dog's life. What right has he got to humiliate me. Him who is drinking himself to death. What is wrong with this man that he should turn against his own son, that he should want me to take a beating? I hate you dad. I'll show you. I will do this for mam, and all the way back home I will laugh at you. Yes that's what I will do, laugh at him. The anger was suddenly dead. It was as if it were fermenting from my heart. It was deep inside of me, not bubbling over onto the surface, but waiting coolly, to pounce like a wild cat out of the jungle.

Why was I born with him for a father? He punches and kicks me and tells me I'm yellow. Why could I not have a dad like Terry's, who jokes and laughs with him and brings him things home. Just you wait. I'll show you.

"Philip, there you are. What's the matter, you look so pale," Mr. Green was squinting over his glasses into my face. "Oh. You're getting the butterflies. Well, never mind it's understandable how you feel, but how do you feel?" he went on asking me suspiciously. I replied "I feel great. I'm going to give him the works", remembering what Terry had shouted at the barracks. "Ah, good show," Mr. Green beamed, "that's what I like to hear. Well then lets have you in the dressing room, Charlie, er your dad is in there." The dressing room was alive with nervous excitement. "Listen for your names and who you are boxing" a man with a Hitler moustache was saying. He read out the names with frightening intensity as if we were being told whether we hung or whether we were reprieved, and on knowing the names of our opponents we were still no nearer to the verdict. I was boxing a boy called Watson. My eyes scanned the room. A boy was putting on a pair of real boxing boots; he brought out of a bag a pair of dazzling red shorts. Christ, not him, please. God, not him. Everyone was watching the little sod shadow box. Mr. Green came and stood next to me and said sadly, "That's your opponent Philip."

We all watched, entranced by his cockiness. I could see dad smiling. He looked my way and grinned. I looked at him with hatred in my eyes. Dad walked over to where I stood carrying a carrier bag. "Well what do you think of him?" he asked, gloatingly. "Don't say that you have got the guts-ache just because he has got a flashy pair of shorts on. Or is it because he's got a couple of badges on 'em?" He went on gloating. "I was bloody right about you, you are yellow. Your mam said you are going to win for her tonight, and look at yer, scared half out of your wits over a silly little bugger like that. Wait till I tell her." I pulled off my jersey and then my wellingtons, and my dad said in a disgusted voice: "Right, on with the shorts". Two boxers were going out to the ring. I looked over at Watson. He was smiling. A few people stood talking to him. Mr. Green passed by to go out into the hall and I heard my dad say "What fight is he on Ces?" Mr. Green, answered "The next". "O.K." my dad said. "I'll look after him." I felt as if I were dreaming it all. "Right you are on next" my dad said in a harsh voice. My heart was thumping a death beat in my chest.

Mr. Green was back with one of the boxers. Blood was streaming down the boy's face from his nose. Mr. Green was shaking his head sadly at dad, then he said "Glove him up, Charlie, I will be back in a minute." Dad reached for the gloves, disgust written all over his face. "Hold your hands out." He spat the words out, not looking into my face. I looked as he bent over me, lacing up the gloves. I noticed the hair receeding in the middle of his head. "Well this is it, old pal, this is where you give me a treat. I'm looking forward to you getting this beating." Yet I could not believe that this was coming from my own father. He went on, "That's my only reason for being here tonight: I would give a week's wages to watch you cop it tonight." He grinned. "It's a pity your mam isn't here too, then she would see how yellow you really are." I felt the anger and hatred welling up again inside me for this man, my father. What must I do? I know, I must win, that's it, that's what I must do, win. Who cares about this flashy little bugger with his flashy shorts? Who cares about me? Nobody but my mam. My mam who I love more than anybody in the world. She knows I am not yellow. I will fight like hell for her, yes, I will fight for my mam, she is the only one who loves me. I looked at my dad's gloating face:- you think you know everything, but I will show you, just you bloody well wait, I thought. Mr. Green came in hurriedly and said, "Well Philip, you are on now. Oh, good show, Charlie, I see you have laced him up. Well there will be no need for me to tell you anything, your dad will have done that" he said, in a fluster. I heard someone shouting: "Watson, McGrath." "Yes, here we are" said Mr. Green, nervously. "Come on, Philip, this way." I could see dad out of the corner of my eye, grinning at me. You wicked swine, I thought, I'll show you. He thinks because I am nervous, I am yellow. Well I will show the bastard. Mr. Green was saying, "Will you pass me the bottle up after every round, Charlie, please." I saw my dad nod. Oh no, I thought, I can't stand him grinning at me every round.

I stood in the centre of the ring. The cocky bugger was dancing about like Fred Astaire. I could hear the referee mumbling out instructions, but my eyes were looking at cocky bugger, and I saw, just like the lad at the barracks, that he was scared. All this dancing around and shadow boxing was all an act. If this bugger is going to give me a beating, I will stand hanging. I walked back to my corner, waiting for the bell to start the first round. I looked down at dad and he was shaking his head and sneering. It was as if he were saying to me, "this is what I have been waiting for since the day our Topsy died; I have been waiting for this night." Fear gripped me for one moment, and then I heard my mam's voice saying "but you won't lose, will you love", and that was all I wanted to show that swine of a dad that I was not yellow. CLANG! The bell went for the first round.

CHAPTER 9

THE FIGHT

I rushed out of my corner, the anger I felt for my dad seething in my heart. A feeling of confidence spread through my body, just like that insecure feeling of dread that engulfed me outside the world of Woolshops.

There was no doubt the extra confidence I felt was derived from the fear of my insecure nature outside the ring. I must dedicate myself to boxing; I felt sure that I could make it. One so young can feel these sensations of conceit, but it was Woolshops where I felt so trapped. The terrible dread that I would never get out. Some small thing would stop me from fighting my way out - the unkown evils that haunted my thoughts. I knew that God had bestowed on me the gift to box, yet what if I should abuse this gift. What then? No I could not stand to be a nobody.

I moved into the centre of the ring. All the time I was ducking and weaving, but going forward, cocky bugger was pecking me in the face with lefts, therefore adding up the points, but I continued on my forward march. I hooked him a left to the body and tried to follow up with a right cross, but cocky bugger was not there. There was no doubt about it, he moved round the ring well. So the round ended up with me punching air in a neutral corner. I walked back to the corner where Mr. Green was waiting with the sponge. He doused my face, the water splashing over both of us. He was chattering excitedly, but I was looking down at dad. Our eyes met. I could see the scorn in his face.

The bell went for the second round, and I was on to him, throwing punches non-stop. He got out of his corner for one brief second, but I pushed him back. I could feel him panic. I was punishing him to the face and body. We fell into a clinch, I could hear him breathing heavily. I tried to untangle myself from his arms, but he held on. I was frantic to break lose from the hold he had on my arms. I remembered the words my dad had said to me, the hatred for them swelled inside me once again. I was not yellow, it was this sod that was yellow. The seething anger flared. "Break lose you bastard." The tears came to my eyes, all the impatience to be somebody, the dread that that cocky bugger would take away the things I want so much. No, it shall not be. My head was hitting his face. "Stop holding me you bastard, fight fair, do you hear, fight fair."

I broke free, the blood was streaming down his face. The referee was leading me back to my corner "I'm disqualifying McGrath for butting. Never have I seen such a disgraceful exhibition of bad sportsmanship in one so young." He walked to the centre of the ring to announce the verdict. I stood there, sick within myself. It did not register that I had done anything wrong. All I had done was stop him holding me. What am I supposed to do when he holds my arms? I felt the tears burning in my eyes. Mr. Green looked at me sadly. I just wanted to be out of this ring and back home with my mam. Mr. Green guided me down the steps from the ring. My dad was staring at me with that stupid grin on his face. I pushed past him, hating the very nearness of him. I could never forgive him for all the hurt and misery he had made me go through.

I hurried towards the dressing room, full of my own sorrow. A tall man stepped out and barred my way. He looked down on me and with anger showing in his face he shouted "You dirty little bugger, what's the matter with you? Can't you fight fair from Halifax?" I felt someone brush past me like a ghost. I heard a clapping sound. I looked up into the tall man's face, but he was sitting on the floor like the drunks I saw down Woolshops. Blood was on his face. A man was standing over him. Crikey. It's my dad. I saw another bloke grab him from behind. I jumped on his back with my gloves still on, holding his neck, but he threw me over his shoulder. I hit my head on a chair and felt me eye swell like an egg. I saw Mr. Green jump in, trying to get dad away. The place was now in a riot. Chairs were being thrown all over the place, fists were flying in every direction, there were women screaming, and dad was in the middle giving as good as he got. I saw Mr. Green searching for his glasses. I got up from the floor. Tears were not far away. I felt scared. Where is my dad? I ran into the crowd. "Leave my dad alone, you rotten bastards", I screamed with rage. A fat woman shouted: "Stop this, you lunatics." She was grabbing hold of men's hair and pushing and pulling them out of the melee. I heard dad's voice. "It's allright, Philip. I am here." I looked up and saw his grinning face. His right eye was bruised, then he said "Come on lad, let's get Mr. Green and vamoosh" He laughed. Mr. Green was getting the kids ready for the bus. He had a red mark on his nose. "How are you, Ces?" my dad asked. "My glasses got broken in the disturbance, but I'm alright otherwise" he replied, forcing a smile. My dad laughed and said "You will do for me Ces", as he patted him on the shoulder.

It was well past midnight before we reached Halifax. The rain had stopped, leaving everything clear and fresh. We walked side by side down the cobbled streets of Woolshops. Dad was carrying my paper bag. My eye was now closed completely; dad's was also closed to a slit. There was a bond between us, a feeling of contentment. This was a night which we would remember for ever, a memory that we would each in turn take to our graves. We went past the doss-house which we both knew so well. Two drunks, holding each other up, passed us. Further down the street, stood three policemen, like vultures waiting to pounce on and snatch any prey which had the ill luck to fall their way. One of the policemen looked at us saying "Hello, Charlie, where have you been?" - "Have been to London to see the Queen", was dad's reply. Two of the bobbies started laughing, but the third didn't. He stood in the door way, preferring the two drunks. We walked on in silence, both smiling to ourselves. A woman stood in a shop doorway, shivering against the window. "Here Annie," dad said, giving her half a crown, "get yourself a bed for the night." "Ta, Charlie," she said, "I will give it back to you the week-end". Dad grinned that same knowing grin when I was in the ring. It seemed an age since I vowed never to forgive him for the misery he had caused me. I even thought that I hated him, but now this love which I feel for the very same man, my dad. What is it you have Charlie? - this magic, this wand which you are able to wave over mother, and now me, you with your Jeckyll and Hyde personality?

"Dad" I heard myself saying, "Dad, do you like Mr. Green?" - at the same time knowing that he did. "I like Mr. Green, because now and again he comes into our world, and although he may not agree with us, he will listen to our problems and has the courage to stand by his convictions." I didn't at that time understand what dad was saying, but somehow it seemed so, right. So I walked, nodding like a wise old man.

We could see the dim yellow light of the gas mantles as

we walked on down the street. "Philip, I want to say something before we go into the house" dad said. "You are going to have to control your temper. You have the right approach to a fight, but you will lose it all by losing your head. By all means be angry, but it must be controlled anger. Do you understand?" I looked up at him with a puzzled expression on my face, he went on as if in answer to my unspoken question. "If someone hit you a good'un in the face, it's no good rushing at him like a bull, because he will be waiting for you. You must put it in a note book in your head. Then when your turn comes you can give him all that you have got." Dad knocked on the door. "Who is it?" I heard mam say. "It's Charlie McGrath with a big blonde," dad shouted through the letter box. I could hear mam giggle and the key turned in the lock. We walked into the dim light of the dingy room, yet tonight I felt I was walking into a palace. The happiness enveloped me. I could never love two people the way I loved these two at this moment. I looked at my Queen's startled face as she looked into my swollen eye. "Well you copped a real good one there" she said, then looking at my dad, ready to cast all blame on him, she noticed that he had also copped. "Charlie McGrath, you have been at it again, you have been on the booze." "You are wrong, Ivy, so help me, you are wrong." Dad then told her the full story, even telling her about Mr. Green breaking his glasses. Mam looked at dad with a smile. "You will never learn, Charlie, will you?" Dad grabbed hold of her by the waist, and said "If you ever get a woman half as good as this one, you will be lucky."

CHAPTER 10

BLACK SUNDAY

I have often heard people say that you only remember the good parts of your childhood. They say that we tend to remember only the good things, hiding the bad, unpleasant, and embarrassing things, memories of which are pushed into hidden crevices in our minds. But I find, in my case, that the unpleasant life far outweighed the happy times, and thereby spreading a blanket of gloom and despair over my childhood memories; but from gloom comes hope. From childhood comes manhood. This I knew, and by knowing this, I was happy and dreamed of better things to come. Dad was by now too far gone in his drinking to ever contemplate the danger he was in. I really don't think that it would have made any difference if he had noticed how ill he was. Dad was by nature and will a strong person, and disliked weakness in others. Even now, while dying, the slow sodden death of alcoholism, nothing changed his attitude of philosophy in life. It was as if he were laughing in the face of death. Laughing at his self-destruction, and saying "You can destroy my body, but never my spirit." "But go ahead, try your worst."

But why this meaningless self-destruction, dad? - why this terrible sorrow you inflict upon my mother? I know that you love her. Haven't I read it in your eyes? I saw it the night we came home from Thurnsco. How come, then, that you hurt her in this way? Is this the spell your wand holds over her? Why, why can't you cry and let us know that you have feelings? Why the refusal to see a doctor? Are you flaunting this arrogant charm, this hold that you have over other people, too far? Or is it your fear of showing your true self, frightened of letting your family and loved ones know that Charlie McGrath has shed tears the same as other men? You can show feelings dad, like the night we came back from Thurnsco. I must try to find out how your sub-concious works. You see, dad, it is your blood that runs through my veins, and it was your sperm that conceived me. I mimic your every mannerism, your attitudes have been implanted into me, and this being so, only you have the answer to my downfall. Or were you my downfall? You most certainly made me a better fighter with your cold approach and attitude, but was this good for me? Was this your bitterness at life which you expressed through me? Did you ever once see me as a small boy who sometimes cuts his knee? - a boy who needed love and affection? Never! Did you care and ask how school was going? Tell me, would doing these things be a show of weakness? - were these little things of no importance to you? Did you ever regret doing them dad?

Here, I have to be above all honest and ruthless with myself. Whilst writing this book, I could very easily give the impression that I was the innocent Oliver Twist of Woolshops. Flowing through these pages with self-innocence, but this would not be a true picture of things. Honesty is the one thing I have left. It's the only weapon I have to combat my own downfall. If a thief blames a fingerprint on a glass for getting caught, then he is being untrue to himself, but if he admits that he was careless by leaving his print on the glass, then he still has the chance of becoming a still better thief.

I was a child of Woolshops. A tough, crafty, cocky little child. Irresponsible in my lessons. I had no interest in patience, or to delve into the intricate ways of maths and things, but I had a love of reading. Often would I sit down and be transported into another world by the magic of an author's words. I was a scruffy, untidy being, not caring anything about my appearance. Maybe I thought I was in a hopeless situation, or was it that I was using my slum background as an excuse? Whatever it was, I must endeavour to be fair. Needless to say, I never got the prefect's job, and strange though this might seem, my feelings were those of relief. You see, young Mr. McGrath did not like and was terrified of responsibility. I just could not stand humiliation in any form. Out of this grew a type of conceit. I found myself only willing to attempt the things at which I excelled. I like to think it was lack of confidence, but whatever it was, it gave the impression of a 'couldn't care less attitude'. My appearance didn't help in any respect. But behind this scruffy, cocky attitude was this dreaded feeling of insecurity, which has always haunted me, and which I have mentioned earlier.

Sport came easily to me, and I was always so arrogant and sure of myself. It was this arrogance which brings me to my next unpleasant incident, or should it be accident? For that is in all truth what it was, and I have the scars to prove it.

Sunday is a day I detest. The mere thought of it puts me in a state of apprehension and depression. It seems as if everything nasty which could happen has happened to me on this one day. I am convinced that when I die, it will be on this fateful day. Topsy, our cat, died on this terrible day, Sunday. I went down with my appendix and with chicken pox on a Sunday. But these were nothing compared with my next accident. If I am to take this superstitious attitude then again, I must be fair. You see, I was thirteen on this fateful Sunday.

It was about ten in the morning when I called round for my pal, Terry. We didn't go to Church because mam had found out that it was a complete waste of time sending me. We simply hid out of the way on some spare ground near there, but would find out before Monday who had served Mass, and at what time, and who the alter boys were, and such like details, our source of information being Terry's sister. She wrote it down on a piece of paper with meticulous care. This saved us from any fear of interrogation - after all, we had all the answers off pat, didn't we? On this particular Sunday, my dad was sleeping the heavy sleep of the drunk. The bedroom would reek with the sickly sweet smell of stale ale, his deathly white face contrasted stongly with the mass of curly black hair. It seemed as if nothing could wake him from this Rip Van Winkle slumber, but alas he would be awake, yes, wide awake, ten minutes before the pubs opened. It was as if all the years of practice had built within him a kind of warning system, something which said "Come on, Charlie, get up. If you don't you will miss your ale."

At this time, Terry and myself were getting tired with our game which was throwing stones at tin cans. "Let's play follow your leader" I said to Terry, at once jumping upon a wall which led up to the roof at the copper works. "No I don't want to Philip", Terry said sullenly; I jumped from the wall doing a sommersault landing in a pile of sand at Terry's feet. "You are bloody yellow" I screamed at him. "No I am not" he shouted back. "Well come on then I will be the leader", I cockily said to him. "Alright then" he moaned. We advanced towards the wall laughing and talking, then off the top of the wall we would sommersault and twist into the sand below. "Right Terry, now we will go up onto the copperworks roof!" From the wall Terry gave me a scared look, but remembering how I called him yellow decided not to say anything. We advanced along the wall grunting and groaning as we went higher and higher, our eyes searching for any vantage point where we could further advancement. We were now climbing the steepest part of the wall! I looked round and saw Terry a couple of feet below me, his hands searching frantically for any nicks in the joints of the wall in order to pull himself up. I could hear him puffing and panting and remember smiling at my own excitement, that same excitement I got when I was in the ring boxing- this was something I loved to feel. It seemed so easy to be able to do these things, but kids get frightened, even Terry was scared but I knew he would never show it! I thought of Terry, when once I had dived into a prickly bush head-first; all the other boys were scared to do it, but Terry! - he looked at me as if to say, "anything you can do I can do" - and Terry dived into the bush! Funny thing is Terry was not jealous of me - nor I of him, we simply did everything together, that's why we were so close, just like two peas in a pod, that's what the neighbours would say.

By now I had reached the summit of the wall and clambered on to the copper works roof. I turned round and looked at the mountain I had conquered! Happiness flooded through my small body, the same feeling I encountered when coming out of the boxing ring, elated and yet wondering why you experienced fear in the first place. I felt it was all so easy! I watched with fascination my little pal, Terry, creeping slowly but surely up the steep craggy wall, like a flea working into your scalp, or a squirrel that ferrets for its nuts! A feeling of tenderness ran through my body; how I loved this brave little pal of mine because, unlike me, he feels the fear more, but overcomes it with his love for me!

Terry arrived at the top of the wall and jumped down

triumphantly on to the roof. He smiled at me. "I made it Philip!" he said. "Yes", I replied encouragingly, "you will take some beating. We will cross over to the other side", I said, moving across the glass panels of the roof. Terry was looking at me with reluctance as he moved up the slats of the roof. "You are not scared", I shouted at him cockily - but that was the last thing I said because I had gone through the glass panel! I crashed down into the workshop and lay like a squashed tomato, blood spewing out of me from my head and legs, but still conscious. Blood was dripping down my face and into my eyes. "Philip," Terry shouted, "I will tell your mam, don't worry, stay there, I won't be long", his scared voice rang out. "Terry, don't leave me", I sobbed, but the face had already gone. I lay in my own pool of blood crying softly to myself.

Terry ran screaming on the street, the tears rolling down his scared face. "Philip has fell into the copper works", he shouted hastily banging on our door. The women stopped in their work and came out on the street chattering excitedly. Mam was distempering the bedroom, her hair tied in a turban. She came to the window. "What's the matter?", she shouted. "Philip has fallen into the copper works, Ivy", one of our neighbours said. "Oh my God ", she blurted out, running down the stairs. They ran towards the copper works, women and small children, mam leading the way, green distemper spotted her face and turban. They all banged on the big wooden door but to no avail. "Oh my God," my mam cried, "please spare my little baby." "Steady Ivy," Mary, one of her friends, said. "Everything's going to be alright, we will have to go get your Charlie out of the pub." They all ran up the road, each step they took more people gathered. They arrived at the pub, mam leading the way to the public bar. What were the thoughts that ran through her mind that Sunday afternoon? There was no doubt she blamed dad for being where he was. Oh, the despair she must have gone through as she shouted and spat and thumped her little hands on his chest. "Charlie McGrath, your son is bleeding to death in the copper works, you drunken no-good swine!"

Dad rushed from the pub, the men followed close behind. There was a crowd outside the copper works, men ran into their homes, coming out with choppers and iron bars; women stood with arms folded, consoling mam. Dad hacked away at the door, splinters flying in the air. Soon they were through and into the works; the ambulance was waiting patiently outside as dad carried me in his arms, the blood had saturated my clothes, I looked up at my dad's face, still conscious but as if in a dream. The part fear and part love I felt for dad was vanishing and an overwhelming desire to kiss him and hug him came upon me. What did I care if he would not let me get too close to him, he was always there when I needed him! Mam came running towards dad. "Let me have him, you drunken lout," she said, snatching me from him! She sat down beside me in the ambulance, the tears streaming down her baby-like face. I looked down at her feet and saw white plimsolls, noticing the green specks of distemper on them! "Mam", I said, "you have got my pumps on." She smiled, the sadness showing in her eyes, then pushed a wisp of hair under her turban. "I know, my love. I'll take them off tonight and give them a good clean", she said. "Well don't forget, mam, I will need them for the Saddle Club on Tuesday," I said!

CHAPTER 11

THE PARTY

A year after the accident we left Woolshops for good. They were finally giving us our freedom! Oh yes, reader, I am not exaggerating, it was a prison we had escaped from; but even a prisoner can feel sadness when saying farewell to their friends! — and at the same time feel bitterness for our keepers! We were moving into a prefab on the new estate, leaving behind us Woolshops, but never would we forget it because we had the toughness to show where we were conceived. It was an inborn toughness that would help us in later years to bounce back and away from the ghosts of Woolshops. Dad had promised mam he would see a doctor when we moved into the new house! He was now spitting up lumps of blood! There was no doubt he was dying of consumption, and so with each day my mother died a little too.

But let me tell you about the party the neighbours gave for us on the Saturday before we left, because I think moments like this should be shared by everyone. The tables ran through the streets filled with jelly, custard, plates of sandwiches and iced buns. Crates of bottled beer were resting on the pavement! The children were tucking into the food, their mothers scampering around the tables filling the chilren's dishes and wiping the particles of food from their faces. The men content in their drinking stood round dad as he sat on the step, suddenly looking so very old at forty, looking up and smiling at each in turn, his eyes sunk deep into their sockets. And they, knowing the sign of death, yet fascinated by its appearance, wondering, each in turn wondering what effect this slow mental torture of death would have on Charlie McGrath. But no sign of weakness did he show! It was as if he was amusing himself at their expense, smiling and answering their questions but knowing all the time that they were watching for the hint of fear that would make him one of them! I watched, part man, part boy, not quite understanding and yet far from baffled, trying to capture this magic from my dad but not knowing how or where it came from. He looked my way for one brief moment; did he smile at me? No, I couldn't be sure, could you ever be sure of him!

My eyes went towards my mother. She was removing dishes from the table. She was laughing nervously, chatting to the women. There was a sadness in her laughter as if she was acting the part of a happy woman, but making a very poor effort into the bargain. Occasionally she would glance over towards my dad, but was unable to see him for the men who stood around him. She sat young Stephen on her knee and spooned some custard into his mouth. I walked over to Terry who was still helping himself to the food. One of the men was playing a mouth-organ. "Give us a song, Ivy", Mary said, sitting on the step next to her husband who was playing the music. "Come on, Ivy, give us a song." Dad spoke softly across the street to her; surprised at hearing his voice, she looked up from feeding our Stephen and looked his way. One of the young girls took Stephen from her and she walked over to where Mary and her husband were sitting. The men who stood round my dad looked over, waiting for her to begin. Terry and myself watched fascinated by all the gaiety and joy on the street. Mam started to sing, her clear soprano voice vibrating through the street. People stood entranced at the sight of this little woman with the laughing eyes and baby like features. From her they looked across at dad and wondered that such a man could capture this woman's heart! This very same man who was arrogant in death, who didn't wrap his remarks up in tinsel paper but gave them to you straight from his mouth, a sin no respectable man should commit! But could this not have been the secret we have been searching for? Could this not be the attraction mam saw in him? I could hear the words of her song so very, very clear, as her eyes searched frantically for my dad's.

"And my darling, if you ever say Goodbye,
I know we both would die, my heart and I."

When all other songs are forgotten, that song will still be with me, haunting my every step into the unknown, her voice, the words, yes, the gift she left behind. Suddenly she was sobbing in front of the whole street. Mary made a move to put her arm around her but she broke away running past the men and dad sitting on the step. Everyone looked uncomfortably at my dad, but dad, his face of stone, carried on with his conversation with the men. "She's upset because she's leaving," one of the women said. "Yes", they all nodded in agreement, but the very next moment they were glancing at dad out of guilt for the small lie each had told. Mam came back, her eyes red with crying; sitting down beside dad on the step she slid her arm around his neck. Dad, uneasy at the affection bestowed upon him, fidgeted nervously beside her, but her hand gripped tight on his shoulder until you could see the white of her knuckles. And this is the moment to leave Woolshops, but never completely, for we must always from time to time subconsciously hint into our environment.

CHAPTER 12

THE NEW ESTATE

We had been in the new house a week when dad was admitted into the sanatorium. The doctor had wasted no time in sending him there after examining him. Another week went by and he was taken to the Bradford Infirmary where they removed a lung, then once again back to the sanatorium. Weeks grew into months. I had left school and was working in a dye house. By this time I was winning amateur titles; my cups and national badges were on display in a sports shop window in the centre of town! My work took a similar pattern as my school days had. I was there, I took home my wages to mam, but it was just a thing I had to do. My thoughts were forever with boxing. Mam and myself took turns in visiting dad. I was shocked the first time I went; he was old and feeble in his forties; he couldn't have weighed more than six stone. I could not believe this very same man had once knelt down to spar with me! Only his eyes were the same, forever watchful, staring out of their sunken sockets, always that cruel stare. Other times a faint smile would filter around his mouth, transforming the stare into something bordering on sarcasm.

But never a hint of pain came into those eyes, and it was this that stabbed into my mother, making her feel so helpless. If a blind man is standing in the middle of the road, how do you help him to safety if he refuses help? If a little boy will not put his hand up to leave the room, what measures can you take to stop him soiling his trousers? My mother was stricken with grief for dad, but really it was a selfish grief which all human beings have. She wanted to prove her love. All she wanted was the signal, or weakness, call it what you want. The tap of a white stick and she would show no limits in her love for him, and so she wanted the incentive to impress her devotion to him, yet she was asking the impossible. The incentive I had gained from him stemmed from his bitterness of life, and his doctrine was "you have to be cruel to be kind". So if he shed tears of sorrow on my mother's shoulder, what when the tears had dried? Would he remain the same Charlie McGrath? Was this not his strength, his magnetism? Or was he just a stubborn little man who sticks his tongue out at life?

The matron had caught dad and two other men coming out of the pub outside the sanatorium grounds. They were warned on their future conduct but dad sneaked out the following night and came back drunk. He was expelled on the grounds he was leading everyone astray! I went to collect him that very cold day so long ago; the snow was falling in large flakes. My dad was waiting outside the matron's office, his black overcoat weighing down his small frame. The matron came out of the office. "Now then, Mr. McGrath" she said, "I want you to promise me you are going to live a quiet life and no drinking." Dad smiled and slowly walked past her out of the door. The matron pulled me to one side. "You must tell your mother he must keep to his bed as much as possible." We arrived at Illingworth, the new estate; the snow was much deeper as I helped dad off the bus, the conductor waiting impatiently with his finger on the bell.

We walked slowly down the short-cut which leads on to the estate, stopping now and then for dad to regain his breath. "Philip, you will have to take my overcoat off me or we will never get home." I helped him off with the coat putting it over my left arm, guiding him down the path. The cold wind blew all around us, kicking the snow up in clouds. I felt a cold shiver run through my young and healthy body. I heard my dad speak. "Do you think you could lick me now?" I smiled, not knowing what to say. We walked on silently to the estate and up to our house, and could see mam looking out of the window as we went down the path. She greeted him in the kitchen. "Hello, Charlie love", she said, hugging his fragile body in her arms. I walked into the sitting room embarrassed by the show of affection, but looked at them through the glass partition which looked through into the kitchen. Mam was clinging to my dad, sobbing. Dad was patting her on the back. "Steady, Ivy love, save the tears for another day", he said.

What do you tell a dying man? That he should go to bed and read the Bible? And pray for a peaceful death? Do you bring his milk for him and wash and shave him? Yes! This is the way most dying men are treated, but what are you supposed to do with a man like my father? A man who shouts because our Tony's too long fetching his paper! A man who refuses to stay in bed? Mam was beside herself with pity and sorrow for this broken man who refused to be broken; yet mam was dying too, the slow death of mental torture for this man. She stayed at his bed all night, emptying the vomit he had coughed into the bucket. She knelt by the side of his bed and prayed whilst he slept, until he woke once more to the terrible bouts of coughing. Even when you are waiting and expecting the call of death it still arrives with an impact. I was at work when I was told to report home. My father had died. And I later learned that mam told my father not to go out the day before he died.

But he went out, coming back at tea-time. He said he had had two halves of beer and two whiskies, but he was very unsteady. "Ivy, I feel on top of the world", he said, but those were his very last words.

CHAPTER 13

ARMY DAYS: PLAYING AT SOLDIERS

I sat on the seat of the 25lbs gun, the gunner recruits circled round me. "Right", the sergeant spat in my ear. "Get the bloody gun layed." I fingered nervously at the dial, then my hand went to the cross levels-bubble; I felt my eyes stinging with shame. I had more chance of shitting through the eye of a needle than I had of laying this bloody gun. "You haven't got a sodding clue, have you?", the sergeant shouted in my face. I looked up at him looking into his lazy eye. "Repeat after me the sequence of laying", he said. "Roughly for elevation. Roughly for line. Cross levels", I chanted out the sequence. "Right, Carter, get on that seat and show this imbecile how it should be done", the sergeant said, motioning to one of the gunners. I slid off the seat, standing next to the sergeant. I watched with feigned interest the recruit go through the procedure with ease. He stopped and looked at the sergeant like a dog waiting for a pat on the head. "Right, back on the seat McGrath", sergeant lazy-eye shouted; I jumped up on the seat, twitching nervously. "Well, get on with it, you little no-good short-arse. You are the only one that can't read the bloody gun!" he said, going red in the face.

I sat there squirming. It was a hopeless situation; it just wouldn't sink in! I heard a few of them chuckle. "What are you all laughing at?" the sergeant shouted. "He shouldn't be laughed at, he should be pitied." I looked at him with hate, the ghosts of Woolshops coming back, not to haunt me but to inspire me. "Don't look at me like that", he said, spitting in my face. I could see the anger in his eyes and smiled for the first time in a month of being in the army. "So you want to play it rough, eh?" he said, marching to the rear of the gun and picking up one of the dummy shells. He marched back with the shell up to where I was sitting. "Off your arse", he growled. I jumped up, he gave me the shell as if it was a Christmas cracker and I had to pull one end. "Get hold of it right, you daft bastard!" he shouted, pushing the shell in my arms. I clutched at the shell as if it were a real one. "Right, let's see you run round the square", he said, "with the shell above your head." I started off jog trotting, my arms holding the shell in the air. I could hear the recruits laughing at the spectacle. "Up-two-three. Up-two-three", the sergeant was bawling his commands out. I could feel the sticky sweat trickling between my bare back and my shirt; my arms were beginning to ache. I could see the other soldiers from the other gun-crews turning round and watching. I was heading back to our gun, the sweat now trickling into my eyes. "Up-two-three. Up-two-three", lazy-eye was screaming. "Right, short-arse, get into those two ranks with the others," he said, looking at me. I threw the shell on to the ground. "You no-good little bastard! Pick that shell up again and put it down gently on the ground!" I did as I was told, then ran back into the ranks. He glanced at his watch, then down at his polished boots. "By the right, quick march", he chirped. "Left, right, left, right. McGrath keep in bloody step!" I thought I must be the only one in the bloody Army!

I walked into the billet feeling refreshed from the shower, but still that terrible lonely feeling that left me sick inside. I thought of Halifax and my friends; I wondered about my mam and my brothers and what they would be doing. I glanced about the billet; all were busy getting ready for the rush to the Naafi. They in turn stole glances at me as if I was a leper. But why? Was it because they were better at polishing their boots? — or could put more bullshit into making their bedrolls? They laughed at me because I was unable to read the angles and degrees on the gun. They called me short-arse and blockhead. But I could visualise that in the near future they would be in for a shock. Little did they know that I was playing a game with them. Just like my father had played with me, and I was content. I could hear dad's voice telling me "to play along with them, let them be fooled by your pint size and your mother's baby-like features." Let the big Taffy keep shouting "short-arse" and " blockhead", let all the clowns laugh at their leader's unsociable remarks and "remember, Philip, what I have told you — a big man goes through life never having been tested." But why dad? Why must I resort to violence? Just to prove my point — is this the only way? Is this the answer to all this, the tower of my predicament, my lack of confidence? "Yes, Philip, it's the only way out, or you must be prepared to end up like me."

I went through the motion of tightening up my tie. I could feel the anger and frustration deep within me. I thought of what my father had once told me: "You have something extra when you are small!" Well, the next time these bastards start their glib remarks, they will see what extra I have. I made my way to the Naafi, looking forward to the confidence I would get from each pint I drank. The Naafi was pretty well crowded, almost every table was full with soldiers. I struggled against the ever-increasing tide of human bodies and made my way to the bar. All around me men were laughing and joking. I shouted my order to the barman, fishing out a one-pound note, the barman planted a foaming pint down in front of me. As I glanced around the room searching for a table, I gulped the pint to the halfway before coming up for breath. My eyes found a space at a table and I sauntered over to it with my pint in my hand. I sat down looking around the room. I could see big Taffy come in with his henchmen; they were glancing my way and laughing; so, once again, they were laughing at my expense. I could feel the anger for these people, but it was also directed at myself for being so small that they should think I was so easy! I could see big Taffy and his henchmen grinning and coming over to my table. So help me God, I will give it to them if they start with me, I thought.

"I heard, short-arse, that they are going to transfer you to the Pioneer Corps," I heard big Taff speak as he spilled beer on my trousers. I looked up with hate in my eyes for this big slob. I smiled, remembering how the sergeant had lost his temper with me, but I relished the inner excitement that came over me. "Don't smile at me, you little runt", I heard big Taffy saying. "Why, Taffy, what are you going to do," I said, noticing the disbelief on the faces of the others. I grasped the glass; Taffy looked at me, I could see the colour drain from his face. He tried to detect any hint of fear in me, but alas, I was too wise to show any such expression. "Do you want to fight? If you do, let's go outside. Because if you do, Taffy, I can promise you a good scrap!" He looked at me wondering how this little bastard had the cheek to front him, big Taffy! It seemed that all his swagger and glib remarks he threw my way were at stake. "I wouldn't waste my hands on you", he said, jumping up from the table and striding out of the Naafi, followed by Laurel and Hardy! I sat back and laughed till tears came into my eyes; a feeling of disappointment came over me. I wanted badly to show people that I was not a short-arsed nobody. I wanted people to respect me, I felt terribly inadequate outside my world of violence. This lack of confidence, this dread of humiliation was something I had no defence for, unless my defence was in my violence. I really had tried to learn to read the degrees on the gun. I had genuinely tried to march in step, but it seemed the harder I tried to concentrate, the less information I could absorb from what the sergeant was saying, and yet I yearned for things to come naturally to me, to rid me of this inadequacy.

"Now listen to me carefully," the sergeant was shouting with one of his bulled boots resting on my bed-frame. We gathered around him like children looking at Santa Claus. "Listen to me carefully", he repeated. "You are going on your first scheme, it will also be your last whilst you are with me. I don't want the Battery to let me down. I want us to be the very best with everyone pulling his weight. I don't want any slip-up. I have known in the past some silly bastard panic and end up with no eye lashes!" Everyone chuckled at his remark. Encouraged, he went on: "There was one silly bastard left his ramming-stick in the breech block. And he was given twenty-eight days for damaging Army property!" We all looked at each other gravely, not quite knowing how to take his last remark. "All you have to do is remember what I have drilled into you on the barrack square. The only difference now is these are live shells!" He stopped dramatically, savouring the impact his words had on us. We all looked at him eagerly waiting for his next words. "So remember what I have told you, that's all". He spoke these few words then marched out of the billet. I tried to remember the things he had told me on our drill. My mind was a muddle, I could remember nothing. It seemed that all I had ever done was run round the square with a shell above my head! Everyone was busy getting their equipment ready for blancoing. They were all excited and so eager, I tried in vain to show the same interest but to no avail, and so once again I was a loner, withdrawn within myself.

CHAPTER 14

THE SCHEME

We pushed the heavy guns into position. The mud stuck to the gun-wheels and our boots. Now and again sergeant lazy-eye would bark out his orders as we slipped and slithered in the mud. I looked at the vast open spaces of North Wales. In the distance I could see sheep grazing! "McGrath, you horrible little man, you should be over there getting the ammunition ready!" The sergeant was running towards me waving his hand in the air. I ran towards the other soldiers away from lazy-eye. I stood back watching two of the gun-crew taking shells from the trays, not knowing what to do. I was so out of place and full of fear that lazy-eye would see me doing nothing, yet not daring to get involved. "Right, form two ranks behind your gun," lazy-eye shouted, jumping up in the air like the twerp he was. We ran to the rear of our gun, my heart thumping weakly out of my chest. Slipping in the mud in my haste I could feel my legs trembling, but it was not with the fear of the gun or the live shells. It was the fear I felt in myself, the constant dread of humiliation that stemmed from my inability to do correctly what seemed a simple thing.

The sergeant was speaking into the tannoy system. Then, before we knew what was going on, he was giving us the order "Action stations!" We ran to the gun, each of us taking up our respective positions. Number three sat on the seat of the gun, waiting coolly for his orders. I knelt down at the breech-side with a shell resting on my knee. I looked around nervously, wondering if I was doing the right thing. I waited apprehensively. Lazy-eye was shouting his orders to number three. I watched, fascinated, as the recruit calmly fingered the dials! How I wished I could be like him, so cool and calm. I could hear someone call "Number four, load". I panicked, not knowing what to do. "McGrath, you dumb sod, take the cap off!" I did as I was told, but it was the wrong cap. I took off, yes, I took the one off my head! "Oh no! Dear God, no!", lazy-eye was shouting with his hands covering his face. "Oh no, this can't be true, he must be doo-lally!" One of the ammunition numbers rolled over in the mud laughing! The tears were running down his face. Lazy-eye ran over and took the shell out of my hands. Flinging the shell cap away he said "Fire the bloody thing before I get a court martial!"

We eventually arrived back at camp at eight hundred hours. Everyone was excited, having enjoyed firing the gun with live ammo, but McGrath was the main topic. I felt sick to the teeth with the Army, the people around me, but mostly with myself! I hurriedly made my way to the Naafi, wanting desperately to regain some form of confidence, even though it would be false! I drank my pints and quickly ordered more. Those no-good bastards, how quick they are to laugh at a bloke's downfall. The beer was good. I drank it down with no mercy. I staggered up to the bar. "Give us another pint." The barman shook his head in a silent 'no'. "You no-good bastard, give us another!" I swore at him, picking up a glass and throwing it at the counter. "Give us another, you no-good swines." I stood on the table and began urinating over everyone around. "Call out the guard", I heard someone say. "Come and get me, you no-good bums." The guard rushed at me tipping the table I was standing on. "I'll show you bloody lot, " I screamed, but I was being hit from all directions. They carried me to the glasshouse.

I was sentenced to twenty-eight days detention, and would be restricted to the camp on completion of my sentence. I pottered around the garden painting the faded white stones of the rockery a brighter white! Yet I felt a peace of mind in the guardroom which I could not find outside on the square. I had time to read books. The guardroom sergeant was not a bad old stick. As long as we did our work then he would leave us to read, or play cards, but always I would prefer the books. I liked the other lads who were in the glasshouse. I felt that they would be better soldiers than those bullshitters I had just left when the drums started to roll and the bullets flew. It seemed strange that they were all in the guardroom for fighting, yet that was soley why they were in the army! I knew I could never be a good soldier because I had no confidence or interest, call it what you want, but it seemed to me that the wrong people got the stripes! The people who got them were the ones with the tidy bed rolls, who were quick to say "yes sir, no sir", but when an officer came into the billet they showed fear, yes fear for this man in uniform. Not the fear I encounter, no they were afraid of the man, not humiliation.

"There you are, McGrath", the fat guard sergeant said, handing me a thick book. "If you can get through that, you will have read the best book ever written." The sergeant shared my interest in books, always he would give me the book he had finished. I picked the book up and looked at the title — *Gone With the Wind.* "You have a couple of weeks to read it before I give it back to the R.S.M.'s wife" he said, his behind doing a rumba as he waddled out of the cell. I liked the sergeant. He always seemed to go out of his way to help me. I think he felt sorry for me.

CHAPTER 15

ALL ABOARD

I embarked on the troopship "HMS Dunerea" sailing out of Southampton to the far east, Hong Kong being my ultimate destination. I stood looking out towards England, amidst the cold dampness of a November afternoon, suddenly wanting so much to run down the gangplank and back home to Yorkshire.

I watched some of the soldiers laughing and shouting. They looked so confident of life, I marvelled at their happy-go-lucky manner. I stood watching for a short time, then went down below deck. I felt so sick within through this inability to mix with others, hating my lonely existence, but hating more so the profound shyness that I encountered when talking to strangers. I lay on my bunk staring into nothingness, wondering what it is that makes me so scared of life.

Was it because I neglected my lessons at school? — that the after-effects have left me so utterly helpless and disinterested. The only time that I have ever felt confident was when I was outside the world of responsibility, which I encountered whilst drunk. Then and only then can I say the things that I feel. Why is it that I have to hide behind this cocky attitude? — forever stressing with violence that I do not lack confidence. Why was I always so cocky, wanting to be the leader in climbing the copper works roof? And persistently wanting to show the other kids that I was the best! Was the effort that I put into my fights due to the lack of interest for the things which did nothing but bore me. I thought further as to what I must do on arrival in Hong Kong. It seemed obvious to me that I must try my very hardest to be a good soldier, but how do I obtain this fulfilment?

I tried to imagine what Hong Kong would be like and wondered if all that I had heard regarding its night life was true. I pondered also with thoughts regarding sleeping with women, wondering if I could get over this shyness. I feared that I would make a balls-up of things whilst making love. The nearest that I had ever been to love-making was placing my knee between a woman's crutch but no doubt drink would come to my rescue. I would make sure that I had a skin full when the slant-eyed whore came to take my virginity away from me. I secretly relished the thoughts of seeing a woman naked, and for the first time I felt my testicles tingle similar to the feelings I encountered before masturbating. I wondered if it would do me any harm and would it affect my boxing? Nothing must come before my boxing or my sport because this was the only thing that I possessed by which people would respect me. I can remember Edgar saying, soon after my dad died, that I must cash in on this gift that God had bestowed on me, but must never abuse in any way this talent that you have for boxing. But where is this God that only makes half a man, for that is what I really am, that I have to depend on drink at an early age of eighteen to give me the confidence to speak to my fellow men, yet when sodden in alcohol I turned bitter towards the very same men, blaming them for my own weaknesses in life. Where were you, God, when my mother needed you to stop the self-destruction of my father? Or can you be spiteful also, God? Did not my father stick out his tongue at you? Did he not say I don't need anyone, and was this not what hurt my mother? Am I to be sacrificed for the closed prayer book that lay beside my father's death bed?

I slid from my bunk and felt the ever-present sway of the ship. I glanced about the lower decks where all the bunks had been placed to hold about a hundred or so men. The soldiers were in groups playing cards, and another group were enjoying a sing-song accompanied by a Jock mouth organist. I stood there aloof, listening to the tone of the different accents, and noticed the faces in various groups of men with whom I had trained. The very same men who had laughed at me whilst I was on the gun. I noticed that at different times some of them would nod at me, maybe with a new respect since I had been released from the guardroom after my rebellious contempt for each and everyone of them. Though they showed some recognition, they still seemed reluctant to accept me into their company, and they curiously kept me at a safe distance, and I for my part could never forgive them, and I reasoned as to why I should. Hadn't they scoffed at me for being a five-foot nothing that was not capable of reading the dial of the gun sights. I wondered if I would have been treated with the same contemptible attitude had I been built similar to big Taffy.

But since I had rebelled against the crowd they looked elsewhere for easier prey. I hated big Taffy more now for backing down than I did before. I walked between the bunks making my way to the upper decks, dodging the card players, some of whom were playing nap on the floor. Sensitive of my loneliness, yet attempting to act the part of a happy-go-lucky young soldier, I arrived on the deck and inhaled the fresh sea-air, and breathed out the stuffiness of the lower decks. My thoughts were momentarily disturbed as two soldiers ran past me, one of them squirting water from his mouth narrowly missing the one in front. I smiled, enjoying the fun that both of them were enjoying. I stood at the ship's rail and looked with wonderment at the vastness of the sea around me, and with fascination I scanned the horizon. My thoughts were broken by the sound of the tea bell and soldiers were rushing to the dining rooms. I waited patiently for most of them to disappear.

The dining room was crowded with soldiers noisily attacking their food, the clatter of the utensils contributing to the massacre. It seemed that boredom had finally arrived on the ship after the excitement of embarking. I collected my tray of potatoe pie with a dish of rice for my dessert, and plumped myself down at the nearest table. I looked awkwardly at the two Scottish soldiers, taking in their tartan kilts, their hairy legs sprawled across the gangway. "Where ye bound fer?" the wee Jock asked swallowing the hot rice pudding, but suffering soon after as his face went crimson. He squirmed in his seat. "Hong Kong" I replied, trying to prevent myself from laughing. "Oh, that's a good posting", the taller Jock said. "Yes, yer will be alright there, what with the tash. Mind yer, remember they go that way", he gestured, holding his finger acoss his face. They both laughed. I tried in vain to see the joke but to no avail."My God, I wish I was going with yer" the wee Jock said, putting his stub of cigarette in the saucer. "We are going to fight the bloody greasy Greeks" he stated proudly. I looked with awe at the soldiers, fascinated that I should be in their company. "Where yer from, back home, Tich" the wee Jock asked. "Yorkshire", I said, smiling over towards them, silently pleased that they had brought me into their conversation. "Oh, I once knew a bird from Bradford. She was no a bad grind, but I caught her going through me trouser pockets one night so I gave her one and sent her back 'ome to her man." He stared in turn into our faces with a sad smile. The bigger Jock laughed and asked "Did yer no have yer trousers on, Alex?" I grinned at wee Jock as he looked coldly at big Jock, enjoying their carefree manner. I watched them as they got up from the table, not wanting them to go yet helpless in preventing them. "We will see yer in the Lounge tonight", the tall Jock said, looking over his shoulder as they walked out of the dining room.

★ ★ ★ ★ ★

"What yer having?" wee Alex shouted as he noticed me walking towards the lounge bar. "A pint of bitter, Jock", I replied, furtively looking at soldiers who stood round the bar. "Here, I'll get them, Alex", big Jock said, pulling out a wad of notes. He pushed his way to the bar, shouting his order. "Big Jock's a one for the cards, Tich", Alex said. "He knows every trick in the game." "Here you are, Tich, cop for this," big Jock said, handing me the ice-cold beer. "Get it down yer, there's plenty more where this come from." "Cheers", I replied, taking a gulp at the cold beer, enjoying the bitter taste. "Cheers, Tich," they both said, draining their glasses. "Come on, yer Yorkshire pudding, get yer drink doon." "Christ", I said, taking up the challenge and seeing my drink off. Wee Alex collected the empty glasses and went over to the bar for re-fills.

One of the soldiers sat at the piano playing the tune "Frankie and Johnny". We both sat back enjoying the music while waiting for Alex to return with the drinks. I could feel my confidence returning and flowing through my body. I drank into my second pint, anxious in my effort to keep up with my new-found friends and wanting so much to pay my round. I could feel my uneasiness dissolve and this overwhelming confidence intruding on my subconscious. I felt a love for these two rebellious natured soldiers because I felt they were from the same world as myself. But to me it seemed they both possessed the real confidence that I lacked, and so with my increased exuberance came also my hatred for authority, for people with the power to humiliate, and so the extrovert would take over and I'd return to the days of insecurity, the fighting to prove you were the little boy who had that something extra. But all the time knowing in my heart that this was not the way to come to terms with life. But who do you ask for guidance? Do you ask the sergeant to steady-on with you because you feel so helpless at doing anything technical. Oh, the agony of striving to grasp what these people in authority are saying, acting the part of a keen soldier, yet hating every minute. And always the fear that the humiliation would follow.

"Drink up", I said, draining my glass. I grabbed their glasses and swaggered up the bar. I shouted my order with an air of authority, grinning at the soldiers around me who lined the bar. "Here, give me a hand, Alex", I shouted excitedly. I could hear big Jock singing at the piano, "I belong to Glasgow", and a few others had gathered around encouragingly. Alex and I took our beer over, putting big Jock's on the piano top. I watched, so excited and happy, all the worries banished from my mind. Surely this was how life should be, free from technicalities. I laughed at the antics of big Jock as he peeled his shirt off his bare back. "Get a smoke", wee Alex said, proffering his cigarette packet to me. "I don't smoke", I replied, shaking my head. "Bloody hell, what are yer, a keep-fit man or something?" Alex asked, looking disgusted at me. "No, it's just that I want to have a go at boxing out in Hong Kong, and I've never smoked so I'm not going to start now", I said. "Do yer like boxing, Tich?" Alex asked. "Yes, I think it's a great game. I boxed amateur back home" I said. I could feel the intense excitement clawing inside me as I thought of boxing and my memory went back, as always, to my father when thinking about this sport. "I'm not so keen on boxing, Tich. I want to save my face for the birds," Alex laughed. Big Jock came over to where we both stood. Come on, yer pair of piss-artists, let's get some beer drunk."

When you awake from sleep after a night abused in drink, are you like me, terrified of the new day and all the complications coming back to taunt your being? The facing up again to reality, the fear that you may have incurred someone's wrath, the never-ending act to hide your true self. How had I got in my bunk last night? I can remember I was spewing on the top deck, but that's all. Oh, how I hate drink, that I should feel so utterly depressed. Yet I felt so happy and confident last night. I must pack it in if I am going to make the grade in the fight game. I could taste the dryness of my mouth, yet not wanting to leave my warm bed. "We are in the Bay of Biscay", I could hear a soldier telling his pal. The ship was lurching to and fro. I leaped suddenly out of bed, running to the wash house, my feet slipping on the wet floor. I vomited into the sink, the acrid taste coming to my mouth. To hell with the Army, to hell with the bloody drink, and to hell with everybody, I thought. Sheepishly I walked back to the bunk.

We sailed into Nicosia, Cyprus. The sky was pale blue,

reflecting the sea shimmering its blueness over the horizon. It was like a picture of some advertisement we kids had seen down Woolshops when sticking our noses into shop windows, when looking at the sweets we were unable to have. Even now I couldn't quite believe what I saw. The very warmth of the surroundings seemed to scurry away your depressions. So this is where people go when they have money. It was all really true as the posters I had seen as a child. I watched as the soldiers trudged down the gangway off the ship, their kitbags propped on the back of their heads. My eyes searched for wee Alex and big Jock. I had already said my goodbyes to them, but I must get a glimpse of them as they disembarked, two friends from the slums of Glasgow whom I would most likely never set eyes on again, yet I would cherish their friendship for breaking my wall of shyness. "Over here, Tich", I heard the unmistakable Glasgow accent in the sea of soldiers standing on foreign soil. "Over here, yer lump o' Yorkshire pudding." I noticed big Jock waving his massive hand in the air, then wee Alex sitting on his kitbag at the side of him. I waved, happy that they should acknowledge me. "Dunna forgit they go that way, Tich", Alex shouted with his tobacco-stained finger across his nose. I smiled, suddenly knowing what they implied. "All the best", I shouted. I walked away from the ship's rails, sad to see them both go.

I pondered over this sentimental feeling. This emotional acuteness I experienced with people I liked, was this my mother in me forever wanting to show her love for my father, this trust she had for everyone, and why this transformation to my father's world of bitterness, the longing for respect, the inner hatred for the boy who prevents me from punching him by holding my arms? What is this mixture of sensitiveness that makes me express my emotions with such depth? I lay on the deck with only my tropical short pants on, my chest and arms already a pinky-red, the sun beating down on the white-hot rays of heat. I looked around at the soldiers lounging over the decks and enjoying the luxuries of the sun. How I wished I had the magnetism of my father that people should gather round me and be charmed with each word I spoke. Was it your independence of life which attracted these people? Have I too much of my mother's goodwill in me? Alex and big Jock liked me, but was it not because they sensed the loneliness in me with their own sensitiveness of a slum upbringing. Oh yes! You taught me how to look boldly at an opponent while in the ring. You were quick to point out a psychological advantage, but you couldn't teach me the feeling of remorse I encountered when the fight was over, the feeling of sadness I felt for the boy. Boxing is a cruel game and you have to be cruel to survive, you said. How right you were!

CHAPTER 16

HONG KONG

My first impulse registered the terrible poverty which met you with open arms, as you walked down the gangway of the ship. But walking through the streets with their teeming population, my feelings subsided into one of excitement. This was a giant-sized Woolshops but much more dramatic, the heat of the sun giving a luxuriant poverty. Mothers and small babies lay sleeping on the ground. Beggars came upon you like vultures, making their pleas for cents we would toss their way. All around you was the noise and bustle, the smell of so many different flavours which the heat brought upon you. And all the time the sing-song music played with monotonous regularity. I noticed fruit was really plentiful on the stalls, mosquitoes buzzing around the filth in the gutters. The sweat dripped from my forehead into my eyes; I shook my head with disgust at the heat; I noticed the soldier in front of me wiping the sweat off his neck. We stopped before the three-ton trucks which would be taking us to the new territories, the bombardier giving the order for us to pile in.

We slung out our kitbags and webbing somewhat violently into the truck for the irritation they caused each of us, and climbed groaning into the coolness of the truck. We sat gasping, not knowing or caring where we were going, just thankful for the respite. I could hear the bombardier screaming the commands to move out. I felt the Army truck moving away as we settled ourselves on the floor of the three-ton lorry. As the truck left the noise and smell of Kowloon, a tranquillity descended on the truck. We could feel the change of gears as it climbed the twist of the hills. I stood up and went towards the back of the truck and looked out on the beauty and romance of this truly exciting island, entranced by the shanty towns. The very colour took your breath away, the brilliance of the blueness of the sea contrasting with the paddy fields with their rich soil of brown, and still faintly on the air came the sound of their sing-song music, but it was only a faint echo now from afar, seemingly to aid the brilliance and magic of this lovely island.

"It's some bloody sight, that", a sturdy lad from Lancashire said, resting his arm on the side of the truck. We nodded, not wishing to take our eyes away for fear of never seeing again this postcard picture, so far away from the dampness and foggy climate of England. I stared in wonder at the women working in the paddy fields, their babies strapped on their backs as they picked at the soil. An old man waved his clay pipe in our direction. We smiled with a few remarks going his way. We were entering a small village with its beer halls and screeching music, and soon we were once more out in the open country with its shacks and paddy fields. We raced on to the side of an air strip as if we had just entered a race, a race to our home for the next two years. Then the slowing down as we came to the end of the air strip, a sighing of the engine in relief that his race was at last over.

"19 Field Regiment. Gunner McGrath, hut 62", the sergeant major said, looking up from his list of names. I stared across the square with its trucks and jeeps standing patiently in straight formation on the fringe of the square. Picking up my kitbag and large pack, I struggled heatedly, feeling the kitbag slipping from my shoulders and hoping and praying it wouldn't fall off in front of the soldiers. I staggered along with the weight of the kitbag on one side of my shoulder. I could feel their eyes watching the brilliant performance of balancing. Oh God! — give me a break, let me start with a clean sheet. The sweat was cascading down my neck and, just to make matters worse, my beret was slipping over my eyes. Suddenly the kitbag violently swung off my back, swinging me around with it. I heard the laughter of the soldiers. I looked back at them, forcing a smile, pretending that this was how I would end my performance, but wanting so much to creep into my own loneliness and be away from all this nonsense.

But I stood in the middle of the square determined I would act my way out of this horrible nightmare of inadequacy. The clown was once more bending down but not with the baggy pants and the painted face which we were accustomed to see, but wearing soldier's uniform and gaiters. But this clown was hiding the tears of frustration and helplessness from his face. Army pants covered the trembling of his knees. He rambled on to himself, willing the kitbag and big pack not to give him any more trouble. "Hold on, little 'un, let me give you a hand there." I turned and gazed at the tall, lean soldier. "They're damned awkward, these things", he said, picking my kitbag up. I laughed in my haste to cover my misery. "Well, here we are, little 'un", he said, leading the way into the white stone building. I walked sheepishly into my home for the next two years, taking in the beds, the lockers, and mosquito nets neatly rolled up behind the pillows. I glanced up at the fans running up the centre of the room. "Here you are, little 'un, put your kit on this bed", the tall lad said, throwing my kitbag down.

"Thanks for the help", I said, smiling into his face.
"Anytime, pal", he said, going out the door.

CHAPTER 17

A WAY OF ACCLIMATISING

"Pay correct, sir", I said, smartly saluting and pirouetting around proudly. "Yer daft sod, this ain't the training place," big Yorky said, smiling. "Just thee watch Scouse there." I looked closely as the Liverpudlian collected his pay, flicking his cigarette ash on the doddering captain's head. "Tar, sir", the Scouse said as he strutted away. I stared in disbelief at the audacity of the scene. "Most of the blokes have come back from Korea", Yorky said, "they don't give a monkey's chuffs." I smiled beginning to like what I saw of this untidy camp. We walked side by side, putting an extra stride into my walk to keep up with him. "Where yer going ter night, little 'un", he said, taking a downward glance at me. "I dunno", I said. "Well, why don't yer come with me and Scouse down Kowloon. Get theesen ready and we'll come round for thee, and I will show thee how we drink in Barnsley." I trotted into the billet, excited at going down to Kowloon for the first time. Throwing my Army clothes on the bed, I proceeded to change into my grey civvy pants. I rushed outside to the wash house, my towel over my shoulders, taking in the smell of the shit tubs with the wooden screen encircling them.

I glanced in the washroom mirror, noticing the woolly fluff of my chin. I doused myself in the cold water, cooling my heated face. I felt so happy with myself these past few weeks on arriving from England. All we had been doing so far was cleaning the transport and playing football. Big Yorky, who played centre half, said there would be no doubt I would be playing for the regiment when the games started again. So on the whole everything was going all right. But always the uneasiness lay dormant. I rushed past the shit tubs, holding my nose with my fingers, the towel fluttering in my rush to get back to the billet, avoiding the acrid smell. Scouse and Big Yorky were sitting on my bed. "Hurry up, little 'un, there's a chance we can get a lift down if yer frame yerself." I hurriedly put my shirt on, tucking the lower part in as we hurriedly went out of the billet.

"That's the Peninsula Hotel", said Scouse, pointing into the driveway of the massive building. I looked, amazed at the hugeness of it. "Yes, that's where William Holden and Jennifer Jones were staying when they made *Love Is A Many-Splendoured Thing,* big Yorky said. "I heard the air hostesses go for a hundred dollars a short time there", Scouse said. Big Yorky nodded. "We will have one in the Fleet Club", Scouse said, leading the way. I skipped along behind them, thrilled at the awareness of things to come. Chinese men would run up to us with their rickshaws — "You want lift Johnny", they would shout. And we would shake our heads, not wishing to slow down the pace in the rush to the Fleet Club. The Club was full of British and American soldiers and sailors. I could see people eating with a glass of Tiger beer close at hand, and massive steaks just waiting to get devoured.

I ordered three pints and waited impatiently for them to arrive. "Cheers" I said, as I grasped the pint with trembling hands. It tasted beautiful and cold as we gulped it down. "Christ, the was great", big Yorky said, emptying his glass. "Gimme yer glasses, let's get some more down us." We saw ours off giving the glasses to Yorky. "Let's sit down, wack" said Scouse, grabbing the menu and carefully scanning it. "I don't know about you two, but I'm going to get stuck into a nice big mixed grill, what with all the bloody crap they've been dishing out in the cookhouse." The Chinese waiter came hurrying up to our table at the sound of Scouse clapping his hands. "Right wack, I want No. 10 with double mushrooms, you understand?", Scouse asked in his Liverpudlian accent. The Chink nodded his head, grinning all the time in his face. "Well, hurry up, yer slant-eyed bastard." Big Yorky came back with our beer. "Nay Scouse, let's have less o' that ter neet. I don't want no bloody trouble." "All right Yorky", Scouse said as he sipped into his second pint, "but they always seem to be grinning at yer."

The mixed grill arrived on a large oven plate. As Yorky and I watched, Scouse got stuck into it. "Don't yer want owt ter eat, little 'un?" Yorky asked, looking at me. "No, I'm not hungry", I said, "maybe later." I could hear the Yanks at the next table, drawling about how they had won the last war, and still I was really fascinated that I should be so very close to them and see them flashing their rolls of dollar bills. "I'm going to be having some of them bills", Scouse said, looking over at one of the Yanks. "Yer bloody crazy, yer won't ever get out of the MCE if yer caught, yer bloody dope." I drank my pint, excitement gripping me at the turn of the conversation. We ordered more beer, each one of us silently meditating on our own thoughts. But the seed was planted inside me. Big Yorky was looking at Scouse angrily but he was ignoring him as he chewed contentedly on his steak.

Yorky became aware of my silence and treated me to a searching glance. "Wot yer think, little 'un?" he asked, tapping his empty glass on the table as the waiter came to refill them. "I'm easy", I replied, staring Scouse in the eyes. Yorky looked at me in digust. I could feel the uneasy rumblings in my stomach as I meditated on the challenge. I had never rolled anyone before but it seemed it wasn't for the money I wanted to do it. It was this inner excitement I craved for, the feeling I had to make up in some way for my lack of confidence. "One thing", I heard myself saying, "if yer going to do one of them, I suggest you let me do the punching and you dog out." "You must be bloody mad", Yorky said, "they're all bigger blokes than you, even the littlest 'un." But Scouse looked silently across at me. "What do you suggest, wack", he asked. "Well", I said, "we will watch which one gets most drunk, and I'll go up to him and ask where such a place is, then let him have it." "But wot if he grabs hold on yer", Yorky said. "Don't worry, Yorky, he won't do that." "All right" Scouse said, "I'm game if you are, wack."

"Okay, listen to me", I said, feeling the excitement gripping my inwards. "We will wait for the one we fancy to come out, then follow him for a hundred yards, then I will jump him. You, Scouse, will then collect the money from me and we'll meet at the ferry that will take us over to Kowloon." I scanned their faces, enjoying the look of utter disbelief displayed on them. "I don't like yer to do it with so many people around", Yorky said, looking nervously at Scouse. "Listen, Yorky, if you want out, make your way to the Kowloon Hotel," Scouse said. "Are yer sure yer don't mind?" Yorky asked, looking worriedly at us. "No", we both lied. We watched big Yorky sheepishly walk away. We observed men coming out in groups from the Fleet Club, each staggering along but they stayed close together. I thought how funny life is, that I should be standing here in Hong Kong, so many miles from home, waiting to rob a Yank. He too had come from afar, never knowing of his meeting with the boy from the Woolshops. And why should this unpleasant incident be taking place? This last to prove I am fearless, yet covering up my real weakness, of responsibility, or is it the drug of impressing people, the craving for respect, the yearning for my father's words of praise.

I felt Scouse grab hold of my sleeve. "This bloke will do", nodding over to the tall lean bloke coming away from the Fleet Club. We followed on the opposite side of the street as he staggered on, swearing to himself. I felt my heart pounding away. "You're not yellow", I told myself as I left to cross over to his side of the road. "Excuse me", I said, ignoring his drunken manner, aware of the clip-clopping as the Chinks brushed past me. "Could you tell me where Wanchi Street is?" I said, noticing his zip-up jacket. "Wad yer want?" he snapped, belching in my face. "I said do you know" — crack, crack — I belted him two real ones straight to the jaw. He half sank to the deck, then toppled over. I heard and felt the jacket rip as I tore at the inside pocket. I felt the bulging wallet, sensitive to the people around me. "Let's beat it", Scouse shouted. "Right, cop for this", I said, slinging him the wallet. We zigzagged off through the narrow streets as onlookers stared at us. Scouse took the lead and I kept eyes fastened on his check shirt, pushing past the slant-eyed Chinks in my haste not to lose him.

We paid our cents on the ferry while all around us was the chattering sing-song talk of the Chinks. Soon we reached Kowloon. I stayed behind Scouse as we bustled our way from the ferry. Big Yorky was standing outside the hotel as we arrived there. On the way from the ferry, I felt real proud and happy in myself for having been successful in this wicked deed. "All reet?" big Yorky said as we hurried past him to get into the hotel. I nodded, not wanting to avoid him but reluctant to speak to him. We sat down at a table while a dance band close at hand gave out with a samba. Big Yorky ordered the drinks to compensate, I guess, for not being present on the assault. I watched the Portuguese girl's behind, noticing the tightness of her slit skirt, her flowing, long, black hair contrasting with the milky whiteness of her thighs. I drank into my pint, not taking my eyes off her, mesmerized by her body. Scouse was counting the money.

As I tore my eyes from the girl I took in the hundred dollar bills. "Hundred and twenty for you, wack, and a hundred and twenty for yours truly", he said, pushing the notes in his pocket. I pushed twenty dollar bills across the table to Yorky, rembering how he'd come to help me with my kitbag. Scouse reluctantly fished twenty out of his pocket and without a word pushed them over to Yorky. "Well, wack", he said to me, "where the hell did you learn to hit like that?" I smiled, not quite trusting Scouse and revealing my prowess as a boxer. "The bloke was drunk", I said, shrugging my shoulders nonchalantly. I could see the long-haired bird glancing at our table as though she sensed the inheritance we'd come into. I flashed a smile her way. "Aye, wack, don't be giving her the come on. She will cost yer a fortune, she's a professional dancer", Scouse said. I couldn't think of a better bird to give my virginity to, and I didn't give a damn how much she'd cost me. I'm going to have her, I thought.

I waved her over to the table whilst Scouse looked at me with disgust. "Hiya Chico, what ya want?" the Portugese bird drawled in her best Yankee accent. "He wants you," Scouse said, "how much?" "Oh, me too much for you English", she smiled, showing the white of her teeth. "How much?" I said, looking at her with lust in my eyes. "For you, my Chico, I charge sixty dollars." "All right." I could hear Scouse and big Yorky gasp in disgust. "How much for any bloody one else?" he asked, as he shouted for the waiter for more drinks. "I charge eighty dollars, Johnny, to Yanks", she said. "Well, there will be one Yank yer don't charge eighty dollars tonight to", Scouse laughed. She looked at him, puzzled, not understanding the gist of the conversation. We went out into the corridor holding hands. I hung back nervously as she signed her name in the book. The Chinese girl winked at my girl as she sat filing her nails behind the desk. I bent my head down to scribble my name, but stopped abruptly. Then, without more ado, I crossed out my own name and wrote in flowing letters "Benny Lynch (Glasgow)". There was something dad once told me, to do with Benny, what was it? Yes, I remember: "Hail the conquering hero comes, surrounded by a bunch of bums."

I clasped her hand shyly in my own, feeling somehow depressed but not knowing why. Had I not got a hundred dollars in my pocket? Was I not going to give my virginity to this black-haired beauty? Well then, what was this insecure dread which haunts my subconcious? Was it the remorse I felt for robbing the Yank, or was it the knowing of things to come that made me write Benny Lynch's name in that book? Why do I remember a poem that my father told me so many years ago. "Chico, my little darling", she said, unzipping my fly, "I think you are a cherry boy." I blushed and pulled down my pants. She walked around the bed, peeling off her clothes. "I think you are very nice", she said, jumping on the white sheet on the bed. I thought, "I think you are a liar".

* * * * *

We sat on the parapet outside Hut 62, the wireless making a constant crackling sound as the commentator's excited voice came over. "Yes, a very good left by Pompey catches Moore high up on the forehead. Pompey has followed up by a stunning right across to the body. Moore is staggering round the ring. Pompey has him in a neutral corner." I felt a shiver run through my body. I glimpsed Scouse staring my way with a faint smile on his suntanned face. I turned my head away, infuriated at his observance of me. Crackle, crackle — I jumped up — the shagging wireless. I could hear faint sounds coming out from the obsolete box of electricity, then it came through once more. "Yes, well, that was a real turn up for the book. I really thought Pompey was in for the kill. It looked like he had Moore in real trouble, but it looks now as if Moore was playing along with Pompey." The commentator laughed — "Well, that's it then, at Earl's Court, London. Yolande Pompey has failed in the tenth-round in his bid to take the world light heavyweight championship from Archie Moore, with that I will wish you all a good night."

I reached over and switched it off. Everyone was talking over the sudden end to the bout. I walked into the billet, exhausted mentally, within myself the yearning to do something I loved doing, and an outlet for all my frustrations. I sat on the bed, my hands covering my face, hating the Army for bringing me to such a desolate place. We were miles away from Hong Kong or Kowloon. I wanted so much to skip and train, to experience the fear of being alone in the ring and the delight of doing something well. How I detested the guard duties. Standing to attention, waiting to be inspected, the schemes with their gun drills, the lack of interest for all these things. The happy feeling when it was my turn for the billet orderly's job where I could be left alone with my brush and my thoughts, where I didn't have to worry how to strip a Bren or the fear of humiliation.

I looked up from my bed, hearing someone come in the billet. "What's up?" Scouse said, as he noticed my glum expression. "Oh nothing's up." I jumped up from the bed and opened the door of my locker, not wanting to start a conversation with him. As if reading my mind, he smiled as I slung my pants and shirt on the bed. "Listen, wack, do you know these sailors are always arranging fights with the Chinks? I know this for sure as I watched a tournament once in the Fleet Club before you arrived here. I think it's run by some Chink. I believe it's run on a semi-pro bill. You wouldn't want to let on to the Army", he said. I looked at him, excitement gripping me. "Are you sure, Scouse?" I asked. "I've told you, wack. I have seen the fights with my own eyes. They give out money prizes. Some of the guys have been pros back home." How the hell do I get in this tournament? I thought — then Scouse came to the rescue again. "We'll go to the Fleet Club and ask around, if you like, wack. But I do hope you can box, for your own sake", he added, looking gravely at me. I smiled at this dark-skinned Liverpool half-chat, who'd joined the boys' army because he found out that nobody wanted him. "You're right, wack", I said, "you're bloody right."

CHAPTER 18

FIGHTING FOR MONEY

The run-down stadium was full of chattering, slant-eyed Chinks. Big Yorky and Scouse stood over me with scared faces, wondering what was the best thing to say to me. I smiled at them, a smile that said welcome to my world of boxing, the only world I knew or wanted to know. The fat Chink came up to where I was sitting. "Now listen, kid, I'm paying twenty-five dollars if you beat my boy. If you don't, you get nothing. Understood?" he said. I nodded, smiling up at his protruding belly. "And if you win I want you to come on the next promotion." Then, looking suspiciously at me, he said "What ship you on?" "HMS Newfoundland", I said with my well-rehearsed reply. He smiled and walked away. "You're to fight some Chink called Wong Pak Ling", Big Yorky said, putting a bandage on my hand that we had pinched from the V/D hut at the Camp. "If the bloody Army finds out, yer won't half cop it", he went on, looking at Scouse. "Oh dry up, will yer, Yorky", Scouse snapped, "never quite forgiven you when you chickened out on the Yank".

I walked up the creaking steps of the ring, taking in the roughness of the ropes. I could hear Chinks chanting "Wong Pak Ling" with monotonous regularity. I felt this hatred which I always sustained when going into the ring. "Get stuck into him", I heard the strong Yorkshire accent. Yet it all seemed that this was something that had happened before. Was that not Terry O'Brien's voice I heard? Is this Chink who bends over to give me the bottle not Mr. Green in disguise, fluttering round me like a butterfly? I glanced round the decayed stadium, looking into the faces of foreigners, searching for a face that was not there, but wanting so much for my dad to appear like a ghost from the dead. My eyes rested on Scouse, as his eyes stared into mine with cold resentment, the bitterness of being born a bastard. He smiled at me as if reading my thoughts. I nodded back in his direction and I knew without any doubt that my father hadn't let me down.

The bell went for the first round and I joined Wong Pak Ling in the middle of the ring. I shadowed him to a corner but he skipped out. All around I could hear the chanting of the Chinks. So far nothing had happened. Well, I'll give them something to shout for. I could hear my dad's voice, "Come on Phil, let's get home for those fish and chips". The Chink caught me two good punches to the face. "Easy Phil, put it in the notebook in your head", I heard my dad's voice saying once again. I waited impatient to have done with the frills, but knowing the time was not ripe, I circled him as he flicked powder puff punches into my face to the cheers of his people, but still I waited, biding my time. I could feel the confidence. The Chink was leaping. It was as if he was saying catch me if you can. The trap was set as he continued to hit me with punches I could easily have avoided, much to the delight of the frenzied Chinks.

He moved around the ring with hands down, strutting in front of his fellow country-men as I fumbled my way towards him with novice-like steps. I heard the bell clang to end the round. As the screaming Chinks cheered their hero back to his corner, I sighed. "He is velly good", I said, keeping a straight face. "You too slow, he catch you velly easy", said the Chink in my corner, giving me advice. Little did he know my act was for his benefit and because I didn't trust him either. He looked distressedly at me. I spat into the bucket which a Chink held up into the ring. I noticed Yorky's tense face, not realizing I was looking at him. I switched my gaze to Scouse, noticing his thick lower lip. I winked his way. He smiled as if remembering the Yank. The bell went for the next round as I reluctantly got up from my corner. Those fish and chips are sure getting cold, I thought, but the Chink was on to me, throwing all his boxing skill to the winds. I smiled inwardly at the trick we had played on them once again. I moved flat footed around the ring with the crew-cut Chink moving after me, then I hit him a right which could be heard around the ring. He stopped in his tracks, his eyes glazed. The crowd stopped their chanting as though they'd been turned into pillars of salt. I inspected the situation and rained blows to his head and jaw, making sure he would never get up.

★ ★ ★ ★ ★

"Here, cop for this, wack", Scouse said, coming in the billet. Leaning my brush on the side of the locker, I picked up the piece of paper Scouse had thrown on the bed. I scanned the page feeling uneasy at what I might encounter. "The sports page, you dope", he said, snatching the paper from me and giving it back to me. My hands were trembling as I looked at the headlines CHINESE BOXER STILL UNCONSCIOUS. Wong Pak Ling was still unconscious after his fight with a bona fide sailor from England! The sailor who went under assumed name of Connelly was obviously in a different class. It is time these promotions were set aside *sine die*.

I dropped the paper from my hand. Oh God, make him pull through, don't take the poor kid. Why must I always have to show this ruthlessness? What have you moulded me into, dad? You with your bitterness and contempt of life. I could hear my conscience intruding, you knew that you were going to beat the hell out of him. But why the game you played with the Chink? Because I had to make sure he fell into the trap, I replied. Don't lie to me, my conscience snapped, you played the game for your own conceit. Your dad told you to go in there and put him out of his misery. I have never liked your father's cruelty towards you, but do not blame him for your own conceit!

★ ★ ★ ★ ★

I lay on my bed with just my underpants on, hearing the snores of Scouse and the heavy breathing and farting of big Yorky. I could hear the whirl of the fan giving a coolness to the warm night.

I thought of the parade in the morning and the routine of cleaning the big guns, until the hour of three when the heat of the sun would stop the work for the day. I stared inside my mosquito net wishing desperately to sleep, wanting so much to be free of my thoughts yet dreading sleep to take over, adding to the burden of rising to the new day. I glanced around the room with the white mosquito nets tucked around each bed like triangule cliffs of snow, giving the room an unearthly atmosphere. Dear God, where is all this leading to, the constant uneasiness that I feel towards myself? The hints into the future of things to come. I turned over in my bed gradually falling into an uneasy slumber.

"Wakey, wakey! Hands off your cocks and on to your socks! Come on, McGrath, out of the wanking pit", the lance-bombardier shouted. I sat up in my bed wiping the sleep from my eyes, the fear gripping my stomach as I thought of the Chink, and at the same time hoping he had regained consciousness. I struggled into my pants and my socks suddenly wanting to relieve myself. I nipped out on to the porch of the billet and urinated on the flowers. Scouse was already coming back from the cookhouse. "Hiya wack", he said, handing me his mug of hot, sweet tea. "How do you feel?" he asked, looking slyly at me. "Bloody rough", I said, sitting on my bed. "Don't yer want any breakfast?" I shook my head in response to his question. "Just give me a drink of tea", reaching for it back. "It's no good worrying over the Chink. It won't help matters", he said, looking at me like father stag. "What do you want me to do? — do a frigging cartwheel?", I said, feeling sick of the whole thing. "Most likely there will be some news in the paper to-day", Scouse went on ignoring my last remark. "All right, all right, you throw-outs, let's have you out on the parade ground", the lance-jack said. I made a grab for the brush, beating little Paddy who was nearly as thick as I was. "Billet orderly", I shouted triumphantly! I swept the bed spaces and tidied the nets, and throughout everything the uneasiness was always with me. I lay on my bed with the brush near at hand so that I could grab it if anyone should suddenly come in. That very same brush meant more to me than any stinking rifle. It was my friend, my passport from responsibility and humility that went on deep within me constantly.

★ ★ ★ ★ ★

"Wake up! Little 'un!" big Yorky said as he shook me. I jumped up from my bed, my eyes searching for my brush. "What time is it?" I said, shaking my head. "It's dinner time, and listen", Yorky said. "I've summat to tell you. The Chink has pulled out!" I looked at him, not knowing what he was talking about. "The Chink's all right, yer little sod!", Yorky said as he picked up his mess tin. "Come on, little 'un, let's get some chow!"

CHAPTER 19

GOOD NEWS, BAD NEWS

We staggered out of the Naafi, feeling the cold winds of winter creeping upon us. "I'm bloody cold, Scouse", I said shivering. "I'm bloody hungry", Scouse replied, looking around at the desolute camp. "I could eat a pig. What a one-eyed joint this place is. Nothing around us but paddy fields and poxy farms." I stopped abruptly and turned towards Scouse who was muttering to himself. "Scouse, let's you and me catch us a pig," I said, excited at my thoughts. "You're nuts", Scouse said, belching in my face, "you're bloody nuts". Suddenly I could see in my own imagination the pig roasting on the stake with the juicy fat crackling in the fire. We walked on silent with our own thoughts, passing the trucks standing patiently to attention around the side of the square, the lights of the billet casting shadows all around us. "Now, just tell me how we are supposed to get a pig", he hiccupped. "Catch it, you daft sod", I said, shouting into his boozy eyes. "Catch it, he says, and what will we use to catch it with – – our bloody hands?", Scouse asked. "You're not scared of a little piggy, are you Scouse?" I said, laughing at the contortions his face was making. "I'm not scared of anything on two feet", he replied, shouting into the dark of the night.

I chuckled at Scouse losing his temper. "But these little piggies have got four little feet", I said, banging my shoulder on the three-ton truck. "Are you trying to say

I'm scared?" Scouse asked, taking a drunken step towards where I stood. "No", I said, keeping my face as straight as possible. "It's just that I think you've had too much to drink and you would not be able to climb the walls to get out of camp". "Come on", Scouse said, "I will show you how to steal piggies. Pigs," he corrected himself as we walked away from our billet. I could see the sentry on the main gate as we climbed over the wall. I felt the excitement after the boredom of the camp. "We have got nothing to kill it with", Scouse stated, having second thoughts on the lunacy of what we were embarking on. "We will find something", I said, not caring, just feeling this inner excitement, and sick to the teeth with of the Army.

We walked side by side, drawn together by the resentment each of us had. We jumped over the wall of the paddy field, sighting the wooden shacks of the farm. We got stuck in the mud after the torrential rain had done its little bit for nature. From afar I could hear the sound of dogs barking at each other. I could hear Scouse cursing in the mud as he realised the folly of our madness. "Wack, where are yer?" "Over here", I said, "but keep quiet while I listen outside the door of the shack." I could hear movements from within — cluck, cluck. "Them aren't pigs", Scouse said loudly. I put my finger up to my lips — "ssh, Scouse" — I breathed the words as I pointed at the hut where the Chinks were sleeping. I lifted the latch off the door as Scouse stood breathing down my neck. "You grab a bird and I'll grab one", I said, as the door creaked open. The hens were flapping their feathers in their haste to get away from our grasp. I stumbled into Scouse, desperately holding the legs of a big, fat one. "Christ, get out of my way", Scouse shouted, as one hit him in the face. "Are you all right?" I asked, changing my hold to the neck of the hen. "Yes", he gasped, let's get out of here, we have made enough noise to wake the dead up."

I plundered out of the shack, still holding the struggling hen. I could hear the voices of the Chinks in their hurry to see what the noise was about. "Run for it, wack", Scouse warned me, as a dozen Chinks came screaming out of the shack. "Oh, bloody hell, we're for it now", Scouse said, slipping and falling in the mud. I dropped the hen to the ground, running like the clappers to the ridge of the paddy field. "Wait for me", Scouse shouted, "Oh, bloody hell, they've caught me." I turned around, listening to the screams in the paddy field. I rushed back, slipping and falling in the deep mud in my haste to get back to Scouse. I stopped in my tracks, petrified at the screams coming from Scouse's lips as the Chinks rained blows from their bamboo canes on his head. "Oh, you bastards", I shouted, running at them, not caring or fearing in my anger. I kicked, punched and threw mud in their faces as they aimed the canes at me. Blood was gushing out of our heads and the mud was caked to our bodies. Then suddenly it was all over as they left us, whimpering, alone in the darkness. We had both once more lost our battle against ourselves.

* * * * *

We marched to the guardroom with our big pack strapped to our back. The guard commander sat behind his desk looking angrily at each of us. "Right, get your packs off your back and double up to the cookhouse and empty three ton of coke", he snapped. We fumbled with our packs as the sergeant glared into our faces. "Hurry, hurry, I want you to report back here in an hour's time."

We stumbled out of the guardroom cursing under our breath. I touched the welts on my face which the bamboo canes had left there. I looked at Scouse, taking in his dark skin, making the criss-cross marks of the bamboo cane pinkish colour. "This jankers is no good at all, no sir, no bloody good at all", Scouse said, smiling at me. "What do you suggest we do about it then?", I asked, looking bemused at his cheerfulness. "I dunno, wack", he replied smiling, "but I am not going to empty that truck, that's for sure." "Oh, I suppose you're going to watch me sweat my bollocks off", I said. "It's up to you, wack, what you do", Scouse replied, shrugging his shoulders, "but I'm doing nix."

I walked on pondering the matter over in my head. I could see the two shovels leaning on the mudguard of the truck. "Christ", I grumbled, "that's some load". "I didn't come in the Army to unload tons of coke", Scouse said, shaking his head. "Oh, come on Scouse, you didn't come in the Army to rustle bloody hens either, but that's what we were doing", I answered, trying to console him into making a start on the coke. "Oh, hark at you. What about you rolling Yanks?" he said, glaring at me. "Fair enough", I replied, shrugging my shoulders, "but there's an old saying, Scouse", I said, remembering what my dad had once told me, "if you are prepared to throw a punch, you must be prepared to take one." He stood with his hands in his pockets, contemplating what to do.

"Come on, Scouse, let's have a go at it", I said, climbing on to the wheel of the truck and pushing myself on to the coke. "Throw my shovel up, Scouse", I asked encouragingly. Scouse threw my shovel up and followed me on top of the truck. We took our jackets off and threw them on top of the cabin, proceeding to make an impression of devouring the coke. We bent our scarred backs, thrusting into the coke with our shovels, the dust going down our throats and covering our bodies. Each time we would bend and throw, bend and throw. "We are not doing bad, Scouse", I said, throwing the coke on to the concrete ground. "No", he muttered, "it's bloody hard on the back though".

We were really making an impression on the coke when the guard commander came to see how we were doing. "I thought you would have done more than that", he bawled up at us. We looked down at him in disbelief. The no-good bastard, I thought. We'd not stopped even to bloody fart. "I'm giving you ten minutes", he said, looking at his watch, "and if it's not done by then, there'll be trouble." He marched off towards the guardroom. We stared at each other, our faces black with the coke dust amidst the half-full truck. "That's me finished altogether", Scouse said, disgustedly as he threw down the shovel. I sat on top of the coke musing what to do, sick of the army.

Suddenly Scouse jumped off the wagon. "Come on", he said, "we're going for a spin". I looked at him as he opened the door of the truck. Then it all came back, the hatred for all authority, the wanting to be free of the army to do as I pleased. I felt the tingling excitement gripping inside my stomach as I jumped down from the truck. "Where are we bound for?" I asked cheerily, looking at Scouse. "Anywhere away from this poxy camp", Scouse replied, taking the clutch out of neutral. I watched his face as he coolly reversed the truck from out of the cookhouse yard. "We will have to go out the back way", Scouse said, looking out of his outside mirror. We went down the gravel road, kicking up small stones by the wayside. I sat trembling with excitement, not wanting to speak, content to sit watching Scouse happy in our new adventure. "We will be for it when they catch up with us", I heard Scouse say. "Yes", I said, not wanting to think so far ahead. "Well, we might as well make the best of it", Scouse stated, putting his foot down on the accelerator. We pulled into a cul-de-sac up to the main beer-hall in Kamtin, making sure the truck was partly hidden by the trees.

The Chinese girls came running towards us as we entered the hall. The place was empty. I could see the girls were tittering and pointing at our black faces. "Oh, Johnny, you have very black faces", they said, giggling once more. "We have been down the pit", Scouse laughed. "You have been where?", the little one said. "Never mind", Scouse replied, slapping her on the bottom, "plenty beer, very quick." They ran chattering quickly away, coming back with the ice cold beer. We both downed the beer like men coming in from the desert. "Bring us more", we shouted, and the pints came and we downed them without mercy. But our eyes would now and again dart nervously to the door, knowing in our hearts that we would be soon under lock and key. The girls, excited by these two dirty soldiers who seemed so happy and carefree, skipped around us clearing the empty glasses and bringing the refills back. Scouse stood on the chair and sang his favourite song: "Oh, dear old Maggie May, they have taken her away, no more down Lime Street will she roam."

Good old Scouse, singing of his memories of home, a home where nobody wanted him. So he ran away to join the army, and so we had both met. "Come on wack, my old crony, give us a song, Scouse", I shouted. Then away he went once more: "Oh, dear old Maggie May, they have taken her away, no more down Lime Street will she roam."

The red-caps rushed in, tipping chairs in their haste to get to the two black-faced rebels. Scouse threw his empty glass at one of them. I hit the fat M.P. sergeant with all my might but soon we were outnumbered as they rained blows on our head with their truncheons. We were dragged out of the saloon and thrown into the jeeps. "These two cuties are sure thing for court-martials", the red-cap sergeant said, rubbing his chin.

CHAPTER 20

MILITARY CORRECTIVE ESTABLISHMENT, FAR EAST, HONK KONG

The cruel sun sent its heat rays scorching down mercilessly upon the heads of forty-eight sweat-stinking prisoners. Staff 'Walrus' had been standing in the shade of the the prison wall for the past twenty minutes. He had watched in unnatural silence throughout this ludicrous game, this night-mare in the mid-day heat of the tropics as we stood patiently to attention, stubbornly fighting off our dizziness, playing small games of survival with ourselves. I could just make out the vague outline of the 'Walrus' as he walked slowly towards the squads.

My first impression was of a kindly, chubby man with his smooth, pink skin and pot-belly that gave away his lust for Tiger beer. But it was the slits that went under the name of eyes that you were inclined to recognise . First, owing to the fact that you had to search; unbelievable that eyes could possibly be inserted between slits so small. To make matters worse in this frantic game of hide-and-seek, bushy eyebrows camouflaged your way, making you all the more determined to satisfy your curiosity. Flakes of silver snow rested lightly on the thick, brown bush of each eyebrow, giving him a Father Christmas look, which he most certainly was not. It was a fact, and a very true fact, that if you had the ill-luck to see the blue of his eyes, you were "a dead duck, wack", as Scouse would say. Well, he got me dead. Yes, that no-good, whore's bastard got me dead for one week in the padded cell (the 'oven'), and they put a monkey jacket on me and left me there, the grinning, no-good shit-bags. But I was not bothered about the jacket, after a while I got used to it. Besides, it stopped me playing with myself. It was not the jacket, it was the darkness that I feared. Oh, I really was scared of the darkness and I just could not move far enough to see that patch of light. I wanted so much to shout for mam but always there was something that stopped me. You think of all sorts of things when you are in the 'oven'. I bet dad will be laughing at me now, wherever he is. He always knew me so well. I am not going in there again. I would rather suck arse than spit in the Walrus's eye again. Nothing is going to get me in the darkness of that 'oven' again.

★ ★ ★ ★ ★

Staff 'Walrus' stood in front of the battalion. I was tucked safely in the middle ranks, but I had a clear view of him between two tall soldiers. He drank once more from the mess tin. As he drank, the slits tilted up slyly, his drooping moustache dangling like hairy tusks over the tin. Water drops sparkled on the tusks as he came up for air. Forty-eight dry throats struggled for spittle. Hatred was in the hearts of all these men of spunk, and he knew it! That's what made it all so worthwhile to play his deadly game. Men who licked arses bored him to his yellow teeth, but men of spunk were to him his perverted thrill, and if the game got hot he could always fall back on his authority. Yes, 'Walrus' was a sure winner.

I was fascinated by the tantrums of this fat-arsed sea horse. I felt fear and excitement watching the antics of this megalomaniac. As long as I was not his victim, all was well. The face would grow crimson, purple veins lined his fat, walrus face, slaver would splatter his whiskers, and the victim's screams would echo round the prison yard. The other staff would hear the siren screaming the warning signals as they rushed from all parts of the yard. They would drag him, punching and kicking from the young soldier. Why, why these outbursts of hysterics; what makes him go into these convulsions? All the young soldier had done was to forget to salute to the front during the funeral march. A bloody funeral march – the old shit-bag goes into a fit over a corpse who's not even getting frigging buried! We stood shaking over this slimy slob of shit, just boys who were still finding out what our dicks were for between our bum fluff thighs. Scum, he calls us. Yes, so I want to stay scum.

I could smell the sickly scent of after-shave lotion from his pink chops. I would love to bite into his purple nose and hear him scream.

The tightness of the big pack was clawing into my shoulders. Sweat glistened on my forehead, its salt smarting in my fading eyes. The sun, enjoying our lunacy, continued its merciless attack. But, with the movement of the 'Walrus' came the hope that this madness would now be over and so the act of stubborness carried on, a straightening of the shoulders and knees and a renewal of our hatred for the 'Walrus'. We watched for some sign from this pot-belly, waddling-arsed bastard to end this bizarre comedy. Yet still he persisted in amusing himself in his own perverted game, a game he could not lose. Staff 'Walrus' was drinking from his mess tin, smacking his lips with exaggerated relish, spilling the water carelessly on the hot concrete, hinting at extravagant waste, this dirty, no-good swine who had not spoken one word after bringing us to attention.

We stood, watching, waiting and hoping. A silent prayer passed my cracked lips — oh God I can't take much more of this, waiting like camels for this evil man to stop this humiliation. Yes, he was an evil man, but he was a man, so I have to outline a picture of him. Like they used to say at school, nobody can be all bad. I will try like hell never to call him a whore's bastard again because that's not being fair to his mother. I'm going to try like hell to learn how to suck arse: I'm going to ask to blanco his belt; I will even take the blackheads out of his fat, waddling bum. But please sir, Staff 'Walrus', don't ever leave me that long again in the sun. You may be right about me being scum, but don't for God's sake leave me there like a thirsty camel again. Oh, it will be so easy to crawl after being with you because we will never forget you, sir!

I heard a voice, but was it really someone speaking? I must be wrong. My eyes looked over towards Scouse but he was standing rigid to attention, yet I was sure I heard someone after the long silence! I watched the 'Walrus' out of glazed eyes, hoping and praying that this madness would end. Black rings of sweat hid under our armpits, beads of sweat ran down the ridge of my arse. I carefully watched a dragonfly rest on top of a soldier's pack in the front rank, a long slender body with large, brown wings. "Are the lot of you deaf?" Staff 'Walrus' shouted, scaring the dragonfly as he screamed "AT EASE!". The quietness of his voice had taken us all by surprise, but with the six inches of new-found comfort came confidence. We had beaten the bastard again, a small victory but victory never-the-less. But really it should have been a triumphant shout — "AT EASE!"

Well, staff bloody 'Walrus', you certainly are a no-good bastard, and you really have put us through the mill, and now I would like to thank you for that six inches of longitude. This morning, and from now on, I am going to think good of you. When the young shit-bag of a bum-fluffed officer tells me in his la-de-da talk "I say there, you horrible chap, Gunner McGrath, I have a jolly good mind to give you a good thrashing with my bare fist." Well, instead of punching this University nit around the camp, I will think of you, 'Walrus'. Yes, easy is the word, just think of you and it will be easy to conform.

Lying there in the cool cell, exhaustion seeped through my body. A wooden board, six inches from the floor, was the bed. I don't think I would have worried if it had been covered with spikey tacks. Weariness soon discounted for the hardness of the board. Going into that cell at tea-time was our only refuge, the stool in the corner at the end of each round. Back home from the heat of the battle, but always conscious that once more we must go back out to the insulting abuse of men like the 'Walrus'. 7.30 — the bell would echo around the M.C.E., and the hurried feet of soldier-prisoners, rushing in the excitement of getting their beds down. The clatter of mess tins and brushes and other items, as they plucked them off the bed where they had been for inspection. They would be placed in the same order on the floor, preparing once more for the morning. But I must not think of tomorrow. Let me think of Halifax and my mother. God, I feel so sad when I think of mam and home. Poor mam, I thought of the letter I had received from her. She had written it to the regiment and it had been forwarded to me here. Tears came quickly to my eyes thinking of what she had written:

Dear Philip,

I received a letter from your C.O. officer. He wrote

saying something about you being awarded a D.C.M. Well love, I can only say how proud your father would have been, but he will be watching you, wherever he is. Please Philip, try not to drink too much out there, you know what it did to your father. The twins are coming along a treat, they asked me to send their regards, and to bring them home some chop-sticks.

Love, Mam
xxxxx

P.S. We will put your medal in the cabinet with your other medals and boxing cups.

God bless you my son
Mother x
Tony x
Stephen x

Poor mam, just a simple woman, never looking for bad in others. She did not know what a "District Court Martial" was. She thought a D.C.M. was what those posh people get for doing something good. Well, she always thought her sons were as good as anybody. Because to her mind there was nobody she loved more than her boys, except maybe Charlie McGrath.

★ ★ ★ ★ ★

"You two in there, just you bloody well hurry it up", the Geordie staff-sergeant shouted outside the two lavatories. "Get thrusting, you horrible pair of shit-heaps". I could hear the giggling of the prisoners laughing at the big Geordie. "Whatsermatter, yer constipated? Are you giving each other one?", he shouted in the passage. Anger flared up inside me at this dirty-minded bastard. I tore into the toilet roll, sick to the belly of these loud-mouthed animals. Scouse, in the next cubicle, sat silent. "Scouse, are you still there?" I whispered. "Yer! I'm still here, just you cool it man, let the bastard wait", he said, letting off a wet fart. "It's all right saying cool it, but what happens if we go into the 'oven', we will not be cool in there?" "I just can't weigh you up, Philly, letting these wanks get you down. When you fought the Chink yer kept cool but outside the ring yer get all of a panic, you don't screw your loaf at all, wack." "I don't need you to give me a f--- sermon", I said, "so just keep your big, fat trap shut." But Scouse was too near the point for my own comfort. The chain flushed in Scouse's lavatory to the whistling of "Maggie May". "Are you done in there, Philly?" he asked. "Hold it a minute, Scouse, I will just give myself a plonk." "You must be bloody mad", Scouse replied. I laughed, "yer, who is panicking now?" I said, fastening my fly and pulling the chain.

CHAPTER 21

RELEASED: BACK TO THE REGIMENT

"How did they treat you in the M.C.E.?" the R.S.M. asked, taking his pencil out of his mouth and leaning back in his chair. "Oh, all right, sir", I replied, giving nothing away. "The food all right?" he asked, encouragingly. "Yes, sir." He coughed, embarrassed. "You know your trouble", he said, getting to the point. I stayed silent, looking down at the carpet. "Well, I'm going to tell you. It's drink, yes drink. You are throwing everything away for booze. Oh McGrath, if only you knew what a damned fool you are being. Yes, I know about your boxing match, I have my spies everywhere. You have a jolly good chance of making a name for yourself, and also the Regiment, and all you can do is get pissed and cause trouble for everyone. Do you really think we like to go to the expense of a Court Martial? Do you like other soldiers to run the Regiment down?" He looked at me sorrowfully, waiting for some kind of reply. I gave him a sad look which I did not feel. The look seemed to work wonders, and he broke into a broad smile. "Listen McGrath, Gunner McGrath", he corrected himself, "that's what you are, a gunner, and that also means a soldier, a British soldier, the very best in the world."

He sat abruptly up in the chair, his knees banging the desk and making the ink dance in the bottle. The proud, patriotic face stabbed into mine. "Listen to me, I have had a word with the Colonel, and he said he is agreeable to let you help the P.T.I. to get together a boxing team for the Army championships. That will keep you out of trouble, Gunner McGrath, eh, what?" "Yes, sir", I said, feeling a lot happier than I had for a long time. "Good show, McGrath, er Gunner. Well, I can tell the C.O. that you will not be getting in any more trouble." "Yes, sir", I said, feeling a little uncertain. I did a smart 'Walrus' salute, and a clever about-turn. So they want a good boxing team, do they? Well, I will make sure they get a good 'un.

★ ★ ★ ★ ★

The physical training instructor was a tall, lean man with a moustache that bristled against his rosy cheeks. Sergeant Bodkin spoke in a slow, West Country accent: "Oi been in the Army come seventeen years", he would say, and then there would be a long lapse of embarrassing silence while we waited for the sermon to continue. Then, when all hope had vanished, with somewhat of a feeling of relief that the sermon was apparently over before it had really started, he would clear his throat and, swallowing on his Adam's apple, he would open his thin lips and out would come the magic words, repeating: "Yes, oi been in the Army seventeen years." While this mental torture went on, the punch bag stood silent, skipping ropes hung forlorn, boxing gloves entwined together in the cool of the cupboard. All the while, unbearable impatience grew worse and worse.

Now the first bit of trouble I had with Sergeant Bodkin occurred on the second day after I had seen the Staff Sergeant. "Oh, you be McGrath, are yee?" "Yes sir", I replied, wanting to give a good impression. "Well, you listen to me carefully, McGrath. I don't want no of your shenanakin. With what I have heard told about you, now, I know for a fact that you be just out of the corrective establishment", he said, as if he was telling me the Queen had just given birth to two buck niggers; "but I'm not going to hold that against you. All the same, I want you to know who be the gaffer." I nodded, more from boredom from his slow droning voice than any fear. At least with old 'Walrus' you knew where you stood. I found with Sergeant Bodkin that you had to play on his vanity to get anywhere with him, so I followed. "Sir, what was it like in the Army seventeen years ago?" I would ask, trying to look as if I cared. "Oh, them be hard and cruel times, McGrath. I remember being posted to India — I'm going back a right number of years now — well, I was the Army champion at the time McGrath, and they matched me with the India Lightweight Champion." He broke off suddenly in yet another of his postponed speeches. I waited for him to start, thinking to myself "God, not another one." That lightweight champion of India had sure had some f--- fights. Every kid's dad back home had fought the poor sod. "Well, I had caught a terrible cold and my then R.S.M. said to me 'you be in no fit state to fight, Corporal Bodkin. The lightweight champion of India, he will beat the shit out of yee,' but I went in McGrath, I, that's right, McGrath, I beat the dirty wog, and I received a stripe for that fight", he added proudly. With that, I escaped with relief.

Days passed unbelievably quickly as I put the team through the training schedule. I would wake the nine men of the boxing team early in the morning, making sure they all wore heavy boots, but during the heat of the day we would rest. In the cool of the late afternoon we would spar and skip, and all the time I felt so happy in my little world of boxing with no fear of being shown up against authority. Big Jock, or maybe little Paddy, would ask me the best way to throw a straight left. Even old Bodkin kept in the background, knowing full well that the team was improving and was going to be a damned good one. It was so gratifying to have people watch me with real attentive interest, almost a certain awe. It was something of a surprise after my failure on previous occasions when I had been a poor, lacking-in-confidence soldier.

The date of the team championships was approaching nearer. All the boys were training hard and intense excitement prevailed throughout the camp. We were fighting the Green Howards, against whom we felt we had a good, competent team. Even Bodkin was feeling the tension and he walked round the gym, towel wrapped around his neck, shouting words of encouragement: "Oi, me handsome, that be a good punch, Duckworthy!" The R.S.M. would come with the C.O., when they would walk around the gym, watching us with keen anticipation as we all trained hard, the C.O. concluding his visit by ordering the cook to put on steaks for his boxing team. "How do you feel, Gunner McGrath?", the Colonel would ask. "Very well, sir." After which comment, he strode out of the gym, proudly in his own esteem, smacking the cane stick on his leg. Sergeant Bodkin would bristle like a peacock. "Good punch, me handsome."

CHAPTER 22

MEETING

"What is your name?", I asked, sipping my coffee. "My name," she smiled, "is Pat Ling." "And where did you get those lovely eyes, Pat Ling?" She giggled, knowing I was making a play for her but did not speak. "Do you live in this village?", I asked. "Yes, I live all my life in Kam-Tin, Johnnie." "My name is not Johnnie, they call me Philip", I replied, feeling mad that she had not asked me my name. She smiled, showing white teeth. "Will you have a coffee, doll-face?" I said. "Please, I have coffee, Feelip", she said emptying her cup. We drank coffee and talked. The more we talked, the more we liked each other. "Doll-face, do you live with your family?" I asked. "Yes, Feelip, I live with my family", she repeated monotonously, in broken English. I smiled. "Your turn to speak", I said. "What you mean, my turn to speak?", she asked, looking puzzled. "Well, doll-face, you talkee to Philip about your family, O.K., you understand", I said winking. "You show very funny face", she said, the slant of her eyes opening wide, like the end of a tulip, showing their almond-shaped, hazel-coloured beauty. "What you mean, very funny face?" I asked, pretending to be angry. "Oh, you got face like baby", she said, laughing. "Oh, is that bad?" I asked. "Oh no! That is velly good, you have a young face", she said seriously. "Well, doll-face, I am only eighteen, that's not very old, is it?" "When I was eighteen, I live with soldier boy", she said suddenly. The hot, sweet coffee choked in my throat, sending it down the wrong hole. I spluttered more coffee on my civvy trousers. Almond-shaped eyes smiling innocently, ignorant of any moral wrong. "I am now nineteen", she said proudly. I looked into her eyes, trying without success to find some sort of cheapness to help me in my need not to like her, after what she had just told me, but all I could find in this doll-face was innocence.

"This soldier, was he a deserter?", I asked. "What you mean, serter?", she said, her small oval face frowning. "What", I began, "Did he run away from the Army — did he go absent?" "Oh no, Feelip, he no run away", she said, smiling cheekily. I could feel the anger and jealousy rising up in me for this dirty little whore. But she was not dirty, she was clean, and just because she had lived with a soldier did not make her a whore. Anyway, what the f--- h--- am I getting so bloody worked up about. She meant nothing to me yet there was this strange feeling that I had known her before, but this was a far different country from my own. "Well, how the hell did he live with you?", I snapped, suddenly sick of the whole talk. "He finished work in the afternoon, then he come to my home", she said. "Well, how did he stay there all night?", I asked. "He give sergeant dollars to book him out all night. Then in the morning he ride back to camp on my bicycle", she said proudly. The crafty sod, getting back in time for first parade, I thought. "Well, what did your family think of him?" I asked, sullenly. "Oh, they likee Danny very much", she said. "Oh, did they?", I thought, jealousy clawing at me. "You mean to say that you slept with him, in front of your family?", I said, feeling a little hurt and wanting to get back at her somehow.

She gave me the feeling that I wanted to protect her, yet she was not innocent or pathetic. It was her simplicity, her unaffected personality, and I had never seen it in the girls back home. But there was someone she reminded me of and that was my mother! "We sleep in a little room. We put curtain up so no-one can peep", she laughed. "Did he give you money?", I said. "Oh yes, he give me twenty-five dollars, and I cook him velly good chow-fan", she said, giggling into her coffee. Then, cocking her head like a sparrow, her face went sad. "He go back home". Then, her face brightening, "He steal from Army cookhouse three velly big tins of — what you say — bully beef!", she stated, smiling. I struggled to change the subject, hating the f---Geordie bastard for being such a fly c---. "Do you", I stuttered, "do you take money for short time?", I asked feeling like a pimp. "Oh no, Feelip! I never, never take money like that." I felt a bit unsure how to take that. "I only go with someone I like velly much."

"Do you like me?", I asked, feeling uneasy. "Oh! you velly nice boy, Feelip", she giggled shyly, making me feel like a little boy waiting for his mam to give him a kiss. "Thank you very much, doll-face", pretending I was relieved but wanting her to be a little more personal. She laughed with sparkling eyes, giving away the clue that she knew how I felt. I did not give two monkeys' f----s what she had done, I just wanted her. But it was not just for the tash that I wanted her. It was this need that I wanted her to want me. I wondered if the Geordie bastard had thought like I was doing now. I wondered if he needed someone to love him. Maybe he was just like myself, scared of things, but he didn't sound scared. He had bribed the sergeant of the camp, to book him out. That didn't seem like a boy who was scared. "Your father", I asked, "does he work?" "Oh no, Feelip", she shook her head sadly. "He velly sick. We grow vegetables", she said. "I want to see you again doll-face", I told her, looking straight into her beautifully shaped eyes. "Yes, Feelip," she said.

Always, she would ask questions about England. What did the women wear? "Feelip, how can I cook you Yorkshire pud?" She always wanted to know things, like a hungry child. "I don't want no Yorkshire pudding", I would say. "What you do when you was a boy, Feelip?" "I go to school, doll-face". "Yes, yes". she would say, excitedly, "and what did you do when you came home?" "I run to gasworks for coke", I replied. She would cock her head and her eyes would narrow. "What is gasworks and coke, Feelip?" And so I would explain it all to her, and she would suck on her pencil and write down in broken English all there was, always wanting to know about England. I told her about snow, and Christmas, and my little pal, Terry O'Brian, and her eyes would fill with tears of excitement and she would chatter in broken English, making me feel so happy just to watch her.

"I don't know what has got into you these past few weeks", Scouse said, sitting on my bed. "Yer start training a boxing team and yer think yer Christ Almighty. What gives with you man, yer don't come out with me or Yorky?" "Listen Scouse", I answered, putting on my new civvy socks, "I'm not like you, you do everything so easy. You know everything there is to know about 25lb. guns, you need only seconds to strip a bren, sten or bazooka. But me, Scouse, I need a month for all that crap to sink in." Scouse laughed. "Oh, yer can f--- well laugh, Scouse, but yer don't know what I go through, knowing that people are grinning their frigging heads off because I am thick as pigshit. Yes, I have seen you having a sly laugh, Scouse, and if you were not my mucker I would give you a crack on the chin", I said, playfully punching him on the shoulder. "Who, me?

Laugh at my buddy?" Scouse asked innocently, "yer must be joking." "Yer well, I don't blame yer", I said, combing my hair in the locker mirror, "but just because I am doing something I can do well, don't say I am Christ Almighty. Don't worry, Scouse, you'll always be my pal, even if yer father was a big, black Sambo." "Yer cheeky Yorkshire bastard", he shouted, throwing my pillow at me. "Get stuffed", I said, polishing my leather shoes with a pair of my green underpants. "Tell me, Philly, no joking, where yer going at only 2.30 in the afternoon? For the last three weeks you have been going out at that time, and you always come back at 10.30 roll call", he said looking puzzled. "Listen, you Liverpool crumb, are you keeping tabs on me or what? Yer worse than a bloody copper. I won't be able to shake my dick without you wanting to know where the drops went. Did I ask you what you did with the money you got when you rolled that Chinese fairy? Yes, Scouse, I got told", I said, enjoying the shock he got.

"What gives with you, wack?" Scouse asked, looking pained. "Never mind giving me your nigger talk, Scouse, you know the bloody score. Remember, Scouse, share and share alike", I said, kidding on I was up to something. "Well I am going to get my share." "Hey, Philly, yer got yerself a bird, that's it, isn't it?" I could insult Scouse all day but it was like rain falling off a duck's back, but woe betide anyone else trying it on. It was not because he was scared — I had seen him jump at big blokes — it was just something we had! I grinned at him but kept quiet. "Come on, yer punch-drunk, fat-arse, let's have the low-down", he said, standing up from my bed. I will get to know and it will be worse for you", he threatened. "Let me think", he went on, "it's not a split-arsed Chinky, wait a tick, you have got yourself a sergeant's daughter, or maybe his f---

wife. Yer, that's what it is, yer knocking off one of them N.C.O.'s wives."

He banged his fist into his hand excitably. "Yer wouldn't be fancying yourself up for a slant-eyes whore, would yer boy?" My hand tightened on the undershorts. I held the anger I felt in check, looking quickly towards Scouse, but he was too busy in his own crafty thoughts. I hurriedly put the loose change in my trouser pocket, slipping the dollar notes slyly into my shoe. Scouse, sensing that I would soon be away from the camp, asked his long-awaited question: "I gotta have a loan, wack. I'm skint", bringing the lining out of his pockets in a mock gesture. He looked at me like a coffee-coloured, workhouse brat. "Whatsa matter, Scouse? Yer only got paid the day before yesterday, and now yer tapping me. I lent yer ten bucks last week and I suppose I can say tara to that", I said, looking at his sad expression. Besides, I felt really lucky that I had met doll-face. But I'm not going to bloody soften, no sir, not for this fly c---.

"What the f----h---- has got into you, Philly?" Scouse asked, staring at me with his bloodshot eyes from all the booze he and Yorky had drunk these last few weeks. "Don't give me yer soft talk, Scouse. I have heard it all before. Yer pissed up every night, both you and big Yorky, and I can't get no sleep, you two hairy-arsed bums. So you can go and get your drinking piss-money somewhere else." "That's no way to talk to yer pal", Scouse said, pleadingly. "I'm that same bloke that saw yer take the Chink, I'm the same bloke that rolled the big Yank with yer. Have a heart, Philly. We can't all get us a nice N.C.O's wife", Scouse stated, unhappily. I thought of Pat and felt lucky she was mine. "Yer, I'm pal, Scouse", I said, happily in the knowledge of how I would spend my evening. I fished out a five dollar note from my shoe.

CHAPTER 23

TRAITOR'S GATE

"Tomorrow I am boxing, doll-face", I said, as we walked towards Kam-tin village. She kept quiet, not wanting to speak. "Do you you hear me?", I asked, gripping her arm tightly. "Yes, I hear you, Feelip." "Well, are you not going to wish me luck?" "Oh yes, I wish you luck. But I think you are foolish to punch each other", she said. "Maybe you are right, doll-face. Listen, I have bought you a present, but you must wear it for the boxing championships. Do you savvy, doll-face?" Her face lit up. "You buy me present, Feelip?" she asked, excited, her eyes searching my body, waiting for me to give it to her. "Oh, I have not got it on me, Pat. I leave it in the coffee house with Mr Wong." "Quickie, we go get it," she said, running into the village.

★ ★ ★ ★ ★

"I feel velly nervous, Feelip", Pat said, walking towards the camp gates. "You feel velly nervous", I mimicked back to her. "Yes, I don't like kings and queens watch me", she replied, holding tightly on to my arm. "How many times have I told you not to call them kings and queens", I said, squeezing her hand. The R.P. stood in the gate entrance, looking down the barrel of his 303 rifle. I nodded to him as he stared past me at Pat. "Good luck tonight, Phil", he called out, still staring at her. "Yer, thanks", I said, getting a bit niggerly. I looked sideways, smelling Pat's perfume, as she skipped along on small, dainty feet. She was thrilled with her kimono robe of green silk with wide sleeves.

★ ★ ★ ★ ★

The boxing tournament evening, held at the 19th Field Gymnasium, was a very bad night in my life. It was my choice, it was of my own making, which I will regret for as long as I live. The kings and queens, as Pat had called them, were the officers and N.C.O.s and their families. It was these people I met with their cruel stares and cold reproaches who made me stand in awkward silence while Sergeant Bodkins told me, in his slow West Country accent that "there be no Chinese allowed in here, and that," he finished by saying, "that be the Colonel's orders." And I stood there afraid, conscious of the wives and officers staring from their lofty thrones at little Pat Ling, who did not want to come here in the first instance. And so it was now up to me to tell these people what they could do with their boxing and their shot-up wives and walk out of the gymnasium with my arm in Pat's. Yet I began to wonder if there was something wrong with Pat. I didn't have the confidence, or was it courage I lacked? Was this need to show people how I excelled at boxing so strong that I sacrificed Pat Ling? And so it was that I asked Pat to leave the gym, the only girl who made me feel wanted and I let her down. I watched her move away as if she had been stung by a cowardly bee, and I heard a giggle from someone's wife as I stood, not wanting her to go but knowing full well that I had lost her. Soon she was forgotten in my pleasure at being introduced to the wives of these very people I detested, but never really could I forget the small back of Pat Ling going out of my life.

I would like to say that the killer instinct I showed while fighting that night was for Pat Ling, but it would not have been true because this is something you have or have not. I was once more disqualified, but I think these people had never seen anyone as ruthless outside the close combat of war. To me this was my war, all this was my battle for respectability and no-one would get in my way, Pat Ling or the soldier boy I boxed, nobody must challenge my right in my uneasy world of inadequacy. So these men of war had come to be entertained, and what they saw was a slaughterhouse. The blood on the boy's face and the mean way I stalked this lump of flesh was not going down too well with these fancy people, so they said I had committed a foul after the boy had been down for the fourth time, but it was just their way of saying "Let's have something less distasteful!"

That night, drunk, I tried to leave the camp, rushing out to make it up to doll-face. I had drunk a fair amount in the Naafi, and was confronted by the guard commander, Sergeant McGorry, who refused to let me leave the camp. I soon settled him by striking him two blows full in the face and ran on through the main gates, striking the soldier on guard duty as I passed. I ran to the accompaniment of the noise of the sergeant shouting "Call out the guard." The next thing I realised I was telling Pat how sorry I was for letting her down so badly. I ran all the way to Kam Tim village to Pat's farm shack; tears rolled down my cheeks as I held her close to me. Forgive me, forgive me, I cried drunkenly. She couldn't understand my mistery and consternation. I told her the bastards were looking for me, and sure enough someone had informed on me; they pushed in, dragging me from the shack. This was the last time I saw her. I was sentenced to six months in the dreaded Corrective Establishment. But I have had more than my fill of discussing that place — and so to my return home.

CHAPTER 24

MY RETURN HOME

H.M.S. Nevasa was the troopship our regiment sailed on. I was happy that we were going home. I looked down at the faces waving up at us and saw a finger pointing my way. Then I saw the 'Walrus' with his wife, a slim little woman, by his side. He was grinning and saying something about me. I looked directly into his slits and gave him the two fingers. I saw his wife stop smiling as if she saw my obscene gesture, but the 'Walrus' smiled as if acknowledging the compliment I had bestowed upon him. I turned quickly away from the rails, not wanting to show that he had got the better of me. So we were going home, and all I had ever really seen of Hong Kong was the M.C.E., the 'Walrus' and Pat Ling.

We were given two hour's shore leave at Columbo, and Scouse wanted to shag a black woman. We drank into our beer and talked about the good times we had had, forgetting conveniently about the truncheons, the M.P.s, and the bamboo canes of the Chinks. The more we drank this goat piss, the more Scouse felt it his duty to go into one of his father's bloody tribe. Soon, I experienced the same desire, and time stood still for two lunatics in the sun. We asked the waiter for a black mama. We asked the women at the table for a grind, and very soon the black folk got fed up with two loud-mouthed Englishmen, but we were possessed with the goat's piss. We were men who had fought Chinks with their bamboo canes and slimy twats called redcaps. And what good was it drinking beer if you did not round it off with a fight? Besides, what chance had these hairy-arsed niggers got against Scouse and me? But they had a f---- good chance. To start with, we were outnumbered. Tables were overturned, goat's piss spilled on the floor. I swung at Scouse's relations, cracking flat noses a little more flat. I threw punches from all angles like I had been taught to do. Scouse stood on the table next to where I was fighting, his white shirt stained with his own blood.

A feeling passed through me for this half-caste as he kicked out at his black brothers. Very soon we were beaten like all people who go against the odds. But even in defeat there was something much stronger than a woman's love, even as we moaned under the kicks and bottles being struck over our heads, leaving the scars to remember our wild days of youth, we both knew that. As we lay side by side, our eyes searched frantically for each other to draw on each other's strength. The shore patrol fought their way into the shambles of the wrecked bar, truncheons drawn ready for any trouble. They threw Scouse and myself, ragged bodies, blood-dripped faces, bums for all to see, into the jeep. I saw that Scouse was quietly weeping, much like an old man who has come to the end of his tether. I asked him if he was O.K., but he didn't answer. I felt an anger rise up towards him for letting these bastards see him weaken. I straightened my back to keep back the pain I was feeling in my ribs.

We staggered up the gangway to the booing and cat calls of the soldiers. They pushed us through the married quarters, first-class deck, and suddenly I felt white hot anger for these no-good bastards who watched with their noses in the air. I wanted to hit out the only way I could to show what contempt I had for those people. The corporal pushed me in front of the 'kings and queens' and I felt that this arse-sucker was only doing it to make himself a hero in front of the wives of the officers. Scouse spewed and vomitted on the first-class deck and I chuckled to myself that I had not thought of doing the same. Once more the corporal rushed at Scouse, lifting him off his feet with a mighty swing of his hairy arm, but I was on to him, hating him more than I hated the 'kings and queens'. Punches rained on his face, making it look like a squashed tomato. Nothing would stop me now — f---- to them all, I was sick of the beatings and threats. They would keep me locked below deck in the hold of the ship. I was told that I would not be given a court-martial because I was not worth the expense. I was scum and would be treated like scum; I somehow thought that sounded a wee bit familiar.

I sat up from my wooden, coffin-shaped bed and could hear them singing Christmas hymns, and I remembered one Christmas I spent down Woolshops and how I had searched the house for my presents. When I had got tired of looking, I sat down on the couch and suddenly, as if someone had whispered in my ear, I jumped and fell to the floor, looking under the torn coverings which held the springs. My hand went groping frantically between the twisting springs and there, with thumping heart, I felt the package. Sliding it impatiently open I found the pair of small, yellow dyed boxing gloves. And then once more my hand went between the twisted springs, fishing out the other pair.

Disembarking in Southampton on that cold January morning was the thing I had waited for. Sick to the teeth, I wanted no more of the army. I was to go home on my two month's disembarkation leave, then I would have to go back to Woolwich, hand my army gear in and wait two weeks for my demob. I was the first to walk down the gangplank of the troopship. Sergeants and corporals stared at me as I walked past them off the ship, not even having time to see Scouse.

CHAPTER 25

MARRIAGE

My manager got me a job at a car-seat cover firm, and it was there where I met my wife, Carol.

Jimmy was the storeman, a chirpy little man with a parting in the middle of his hair. There must have been at least fifty women at the car-seat cover firm, and so it was with a feeling of shyness that I went up in the lift with my four-wheel cart. Jimmy had told me that I had to go to the other end of the room. When I reached the top of the lift, I stared in at the glass mirror which was fitted into the lift, fear making me want to push the button and descend back down. As the lift abruptly stopped, I combed my hair nervously as I peeped out of the thin crack in the lift, looking down the row of sewing machines. What had Jimmy told me? Oh yes, I must walk down the rows of machinists and at the end of the room would be a counter. Yes, there is the counter, I thought, as I looked through the half-opened lift door. Oh, and there is the blonde girl behind the counter. I could just see her blonde head as she sat at a desk writing.

I could feel myself trembling as I prepared myself to leave the lift. Jimmy had said her name was Carol. Well, here goes — I struggled with the cart as I steered it out of the lift, the wheels of webbing rolling off the cart in all directions. I lunged, falling over the cart. "Here yer are, luv! Let me give you a hand", a plump woman of middle age said, as she picked one of the wheels of webbing piping up from where it had rolled under her machine, showing long white bloomers as she did so. Heads turned in my direction as the women giggled at the new employee. I could feel the heat of a blush creep up from my neck. "Now, now, Hilda! Give us a chance to have a look at him", a woman at the other side of the room shouted, to a chorus of laughter. I thanked Hilda for retrieving my webbing wheel as if she had given me back my sight. "It's all right, luv. Come on, dear, I'll give you a hand. It's a bit awkward for you", she said, holding on to one end of the cart. "No, it's all right", I stuttered, feeling an absolute fool walking down the room past the giggling women with fat Hilda pushing the cart.

"Hey, Flo, have you seen Hilda with her new boyfriend", the woman on the left shouted. Hilda was saying "Take no notice of them, luv. They are only jealous." I could feel the heat rush into my cheeks, and the blonde girl, Carol was the only one not laughing as I handed up the webbing wheels and requisition form. "Have you just started here?", she asked. "Yet I am working with Jimmy", I replied, looking into the largest pair of eyes I had ever seen. "Oh, you must be the boxer that Tommy Miller got a job for here", she stated. "Yes", I answered, looking at her tits. "I saw your picture in the paper with him" (meaning Tommy Miller), she said. "I think it's a silly sport, getting your face punched", she went on, going to her desk and writing something down. I kept silent enjoying the thrill of just looking at her. She looked up from the desk waiting for a reply, then said, "Tell Jimmy we are running out of leopard skin." And that was me dismissed. I walked down the path of sewing machines, thinking of the blonde with the big eyes.

I now had the feeling that it was now or never to be somebody. At twenty-one I was surely at my peak. And so it was that I went about my work and aims of fulfilling my dreams. I had a drink but always with moderation, thinking that I must not throw away this chance, but I found that drink helped me to get over my shyness. My name was frequently in the local paper, and I found that people seemed to take an interest in me, not excluding girls. I secretly enjoyed their glances but was struck dumb when they spoke to me. Most of my time was taken up with my boxing training. I had won my first nine professional fights, and I found that respectable people would stop me on the town and wish me luck. I knew that I was nearing my target of being a respectable citizen.

Carol, the goodlooking blonde girl, seemed to take more time to talk to me and I found out she was a very intelligent girl. She told me she was the only one in her family. It seemed to me that this was the girl I had dreamed about as I lay on my bed in those Woolshop days. But was she too far out of my reach? No, I must not think that. I must have confidence in myself. I am going to be somebody — yet I always feel so dirty and untidy when I'm standing talking to her as if she is giving me this privilege of being in her company. I found she could say hurtful things without noticing she had said anything wrong. "I don't like him, Phil, his breath smells", or "Why don't you wash your hands when you have been to the toilet?", and I would at first blush and then feel anger. But never could I find anything to say. What could I say? Deep down I knew that she was not the girl for me, but she was going to be a symbol of my coming success. She was a lovely girl, she could talk intelligently, she could teach me how to hold my fish knife, she could add my tax forms up. After a fight she was making a play for me because I was becoming the golden boy of the town. I had watched her do everything so efficiently with a confidence that I envied, but the more she gave the impression she was playing hard to get, the more she set her trap to fall into my plans for the future.

The first time Carol took me to see her mother was rather an embarrassing experience for me. She had given me the hint at work that there was a good picture on at the Regal, and I had agreed to have tea at her mother's and then see the picture. Her mother was a slim, attractive woman in her early forties. I was bombarded with questions regarding my future. "Where do you live, Phil?" she asked me, and I replied "On the new estate, Illingworth." "Have you always lived there?" she asked. "No, I was born down Woolshops", I replied, with somewhat of pride and stubbornness. I saw the eyes flutter with shock, then quickly the changing of the subject. "Do you like boxing, Phil?" she asked, getting up from the chair in her smart, green slacks. "Yes", I said, feeling ill-at-ease. She left the lounge and I could hear her preparing the tea. I picked up the evening paper in my endeavour to avoid entering any further conversation. Carol was fussing in the kitchen, making the tea. I looked up from my paper around the room, noticing the bright red carpet, small animal trinkets on the fireshelf. It was a beautiful bungalow with large bay windows looking out on to a neat well-trimmed lawn. I thought of our house, the prefab, the struggle mam had gone through with three boys, and yet here I was planning my assault on the upper class. There in the kitchen was a girl who had everything she wanted, who had gone to college, and walked with self-assurance because that was the only way you could walk when you had good shoes. She had never had to worry when it came to her turn to take her food parcel to school at Christmas. She was lucky, and God bless her for her luck, but I wanted her and I would have her.

"Phil, how do you like your steak?" The voice of Carol's mother came from the kitchen. A smile crossed my face of days when Scouse and I would shout our orders out in Hong Kong. "Rare, please, Mrs. eh Greenside", I stammered. I could smell the aroma coming from the kitchen and once more Carol's mother was talking. "What is your *non-de-plume,* Phil?" she shouted from the kithen. I heard loud and clear but forced myself to read the paper. Silence reigned on in the kitchen, but I sought desperately to find the meaning of those strange words. *Non-de-plume,* Christ, what does she think I am, a f--- French bastard? I looked up from my paper and Mrs. Greenside was by the side of my chair. "Oh, are you reading the paper, Phil?", she said, knowing full f--- well that I was. "Oh no, Mrs. Greenside", I said, getting up from my chair. "Don't get up, Phil, tea is not ready yet. I was just asking you in the kitchen if you had a non-de-plume?" Panic was all around me — the dreaded words were out. I blushed, I squirmed, trying in vain for words to come to my lips but nothing would arrive, and while this pathetic show of ignorance on my part was going on, she watched, giving no mercy or help. It was as if she was shaking her head and saying "you have failed the test". Carol came in to tell us both tea was ready, and if nothing else came of our marriage in the future, I will always thank her for that.

We planned our marriage after the fight with Drave Croll, the Scottish Featherweight Champion. If I beat this boy I would have been well up in the British ratings, so I trained hard for the fight. Carol was pregnant but we had arranged our marriage long before this incident. I did not love Carol in the same way I had loved Pat Ling. She was too self-confident for me to love her with any tenderness, but that, after all, was what I had married her for, this self-confidence, to compensate for my lack of it. It was not hard to marry Carol without love. Plenty of men would have given their right hand for just a glance from her, but for me I just could not find any depth in my emotion for her. She was too self-contained. I searched for another woman like my mother, someone who could love me deeply, but I couldn't marry that person because it would end my plans. I would be involved too emotionally. She would cry and worry over my cut eyes I received in my boxing matches. I did not want anyone who would interfere with my boxing. I had waited too long for this.

The church was packed with Carol's people, and my people, folk from the fight game. My manager was there with a couple of fighters from my stable. I had beaten Dave Croll on points and the money went for our honeymoon in Blackpool. I saw my pals I had gone to school with. I looked at mam as I walked into the church. Her baby-face was lined with the worries of yester-years, but happiness was in her eyes that her son was marrying this lovely girl. I felt a tinge of guilt for what I was doing. Mam could never grasp or even imagine what I was doing. All marriages were because you loved a person. She was steeped in such Catholicism, for better or for worse, that was her religion. But I could not live in those conditions, I must taste the better.

We had a good honeymoon. We spent our money freely. No worries of the future – Carol's mother had got us fixed up with a small cottage outside of Halifax and had spent money on getting it fixed up. For us, I drank far too much beer but always was the thought that this, was after all, our honeymoon. We made love with stereotype regularity. There was a controlled passion in her act. I put this down to inexperience but my vanity was wounded. But we were both happy in as far as two young people with money in our pockets and physical attraction for each other could be, but I had too much of my father's insight to be kidded that she had married me for me alone. I was the boy that the town was talking about. I looked a good prospect. Well, we were both playing the game of snobbery.

CHAPTER 26

SUSPENSION

There was no doubt about boxing helping me in my shyness. Halifax, Victoria Hall was packed the night I fought Alf Cotton of Preston. Councillors and business men were there, red faces and fat bellies, all come to see Phil McGrath from Woolshops winning fight after fight because it meant being somebody. And there they were, a couple of hundred people of the town, standing in the entrance to the Victory Hall. A memory passed through me of the time I was sixteen when I was barred in this very same hall for fighting, and now all the bigwigs were there to watch me fight. I thought about a prominent butcher in the town who would shout me into the shop and give me parcels of sirloin steak and introduce me to his customers proudly. And always I encountered a feeling that I was being a traitor to my own kind, a feeling of falseness. This is what I had craved for, respectability, but I must never change.

While I was successfully winning my fights, always came the need for alcohol. Strangers would stop me in the town and they would be full of praise for my boxing successes. Respectable citizens and businessmen would shake me by the hand, and I would shake, embarrassment clawing inside me. But stronger still was my fear of humiliation from my shyness. So to my rescue was my aggressive attitude waiting in the wings for his cue to begin, that same aggressiveness that was derived from my father. So, in actual fact, I am the ventriloquist's dummy waiting for my master to feed me the lines, so my memory comes into play. I remember his uncomplicated way, the cool and easy manner he used through life (was this arrogance?). Did he have the secret, keeping his misery to himself but now and again hinting what it might be? Well, my confidence comes from boxing. I will show them my arrogance through boxing and so I will cover my fear of life that way.

But somehow I noticed that people were looking uneasily my way. It was not the way they looked at him. I had to find the secret of his magnestism. I wanted so much for people to love me but wasn't succeeding. I just knew the secret was not here, leaving them to say how big-headed I was. And so came the jealousy for my father, mingled with despair and bitterness for these fair-weather back slappers. Oh, that I could see my opponent, like in the boxing ring, so I could punch them to defeat. But this fear, this uneasiness was lurking never far away, too cowardly to come out into the open and fight fair yet too evil to leave me in peace. And so my friend booze would help me to fight the unknown enemy. Anyone that took away the fear and uneasiness must surely be a friend. With just the right amount of drink inside me I could see what looked like magnetism in people's eyes that stand around the bar. It was as if I became part of my mother with her gay, lovely nature, with a sprinkling of dad's insight and certainty of life always there to steady mam's happy giddiness. But soon the alcohol had become my betrayer, as I stumbled drunkenly over the line of respectability.

But I was at last free from my father's image. I no longer stuttered shy answers in reply to my fellow men. The unknown fear had vanished, drowned in bitterness, jealousy and alcohol. But at least this was me, this was the way I was and, God knows why or how, but I had shed the image of him for those few hours. The act was over, the drink had left me naked. Jekyll had turned to Hyde, but to me Hyde was me, the monster who comes out in the hours of drink. The cloak of falseness had been shed, all my bottled-up emotions and inadequacy being released, and people stumbled back in horror that this young man who had been so happy-go-lucky just moments ago should have changed into a very unpleasant young man indeed. Now it seemed that they were the false set as they plied me with stupid questions. Because I was in the public eye, they felt they had to find out more about me, so the mechanical questions flowed from their lips like a defending barrister helping his client to get through his cross-questioning. But they were stock questions and all they needed were stock replies.

But drink had put a stop to all that. Why should I say the things what they wanted me to say? It was a bloody disease, this wanting to be liked. "Well, shit to that because I'm going to win my next fight. What the f--- do you think I'm going down London for — to see Prince Philip? If I can hit the bastard in the cobblers without the Ref. seeing me, well you bet yer bleeding life I will." "Don't you feel scared when you are going to the fight?" "Yer, I get scared the bloke don't turn up and we get no money. There was this kid in the army — he must have been a Catholic or summat — well, he used to make the sign of the cross, yer know what I mean, don't yer? Well, I waited for the start of the second round to start, and sure enough he did it again. I rushed across and give him a good belt on the chops. And down he went like a sack of spuds." I knew the effect it had on them, I knew the disgust and remorse I would feel in the morning. But nothing mattered now. I felt cut off from worries and fears. This was a few hours of independence, it did not matter if these people did not like me; as long as I was successful in the ring they would still take notice. Maybe it was better not to be liked. Maybe there was a magnetism in a whole body of people not liking you. Yes, that was far easier, to be disliked or even hated but still respected. It had never got my dad anywhere, being liked.

★ ★ ★ ★ ★

I had already fought Hignett, my first professional fight, and was fortunate to come away with a draw. So now I was fighting him at the Free Trade Hall, Manchester, and I wanted so much to beat him this time. This was my first fight with my new manager and this made it doubly important. Mr. Jimmy Lumb was a scrap dealer from Castleford, and this fight was my best pay-day so far, so a lot depended on me winning for my climb up the ladder. I had been working in the mornings up until dinner hour at my manager's scrapyard. Dinner time would take me to my digs or lodgings where I would write a quick letter to Carol who was staying at her mother's in Halifax. Then I would make my way to the gym for a couple of hours training. Afterwards I would scrub the floors of the house I had bought. I felt so proud that this was mine — £1,800 it was costing me — but this was a dream I had always had come true. Carol was having our first child. I would look out from the empty bedrooms to the neat lawns and, yes, two weather-beaten apple trees, marvelling that these were mine. But there was emptiness below the surface, a kind of uneasiness that this was not really what I had visualised. Something was missing that blunted my excitement. I had a lovely wife who would no doubt have a lovely baby. I had bought my own house at the age of twenty-two. But it was as if it was meaningless, like a mountaineer who reaches the summit but finds the view far from his expectations. There was a sadness for the crevices and ridges while climbing his mountain. Those apple trees out there bore fruit that were wrinkled and green, not the rosy red of my childhood dreams. What was I searching for?

When I saw Carol after my fights, bringing with me the bruises and cuts of battle, I wanted her to say "Phil, don't fight again", and maybe then I could be my father for one brief moment: "Save the tears for another day." But she took the stitches from my eyebrows with cool efficiency and she cut my hair neatly before the fight, so I suppose I should have been grateful and lucky that I had somebody like her, but I was not.

The car sped towards Manchester. I sat back comfortably in my seat, looking out of the window, leaving behind the slag pits of Castleford, my adopted town, the dusty roads reminding me that I was lucky, I could get away. The engine of the Humber Snipe purred gently, making known how silent the car was. I was a stranger in this pit town. Circumstances had brought me here but there was no bond that I shared with these warm-hearted people. I wanted so much to hear the shouts of acknowledgement from the people I had known all my life. I missed seeing my mother, always sad nowadays. Gone were her days of singing in the streets, but gone also were the streets. Here I was in the prime of my life, sitting with a wealthy scrap dealer, and all I felt was sadness. Boxing to Jimmy Lumb was a hobby. He liked the acclaim that went with this brutal hobby, and so in a way we were alike. He was a good manager as far as getting you a good pay day. I had listened while he bargained on the 'phone. "For this fight to the matchmaker I want £300, Micky", he would shout into the 'phone. I would watch with admiration, but nevertheless uneasy admiration, as he stuck to his guns and I was grateful for his confidence in me as a fighter. The 'phone rattled in the cradle. "Phone me back later when you have decided", Jimmy said, smiling across at me, and that smile told me not to worry. We sat there in his cosy bungalow waiting with a grim expectancy for the telephone to ring. When it rang it was as if a bomb had exploded around the room, and I thought how marvellous it was to be able to put the 'phone down.

"Well, Phil, wait until your Carol sees the house you have bought her, lad", Jimmy said, drowning the purring engine and breaking the silence. "Have you phoned her yet, lad?" he asked, reaching for the lighter on the dashboard. "Yes", I said, thinking of the conversation we had had yesterday.

"Hello Carol, Phil here", I said, feeling pleased with myself. Her voice came through, slow, free from emotion. "Yes, Phil, this is Carol speaking", as if I was still talking to the operator. "Carol, I have great news for you. I have bought a house." "You have what?" she said, precisely. "I have bought a bloody house", I shouted, wanting her to capture my excitement. "Don't swear at me. Are you going mad on the 'phone?" she said in her neat and unhurried voice, not even mentioning the house of my dreams, this woman who was as cold as a dead fish. I had lain beneath dirty overcoats and trembled with my own thoughts of one day coming to this, why couldn't she whoop with delight with my good news? Twenty-two and I had my own house — but to Carol this was nothing, she was already in a house just as good. I blamed myself, dad would have told me that she did not belong to my world. "I'm sorry Carol," I said, feeling like a juvenile delinquent, but if I had not spoken the line would have stayed dead. "Well, don't get cross with me", she said, with no trace of anger. Don't this, don't that, don't drop your peas on the restaurant table, don't wake me up for it. "I'm sorry", I said again, sick of the conversation, what little there was, the tension of the fight beginning to show. "I will have to see it for myself", she said. "See what?" I said, hardly listening. "The house, silly", she said. "Oh yes, well, I will have to go now, Carol. Goodbye", I said, putting the 'phone down.

CHAPTER 27

THE FIGHT

"How am I doing, Jimmy?" I said, sitting down on the stool. Jimmy's silver hair brushed my eyes as I blinked them shut. "Not so good son," he said sadly. "What yer mean?" I said, fear gripping me as panic came also. "You have been down three times." What's this man saying? "Listen, Phil, you must keep moving towards your right — remember he is a southpaw. And you must stay away from that left, so keep out of his firing range by moving towards your right." I nodded in disbelief. No-one before had put me on the canvas and now I was in a state of shock that my world was beginning to crumble. But I must not let it, now I must not fail.

The bell sounded for the second round and I sought the words that Jimmy had told me — keep to your left — I fumbled uncertainly through each round, just intent on studying the situation. Slowly but surely I mastered his southpaw stance and the confidence began to come back to me. Jimmy became more cheerful each round. I jabbed and moved, not wanting to take risks, always beating him to the punch. And so I beat Hignett, but he had taught me a lesson, making me realise that the road was still a long and bloody one.

The fight with Hignett had been a punishing one. In the early rounds I had taken a bad beating, my eye was bruised, but I insisted that I would be well for my next fight in a week's time. The money was coming in and I had had worse beatings from my dad. I paid Jimmy the deposit of £200 he had loaned me and set out for Halifax, telling Jimmy the Newcastle fight was on. I had about £80 on me to give Carol for the house.

Dregs of the football crowd were still to be seen in the centre of Leeds with their noisy rattles and coloured scarves. I got off the Castleford bus — my catching the Halifax bus meant a walk across the other end of the town. I pulled the collar of my sheepskin coat over my neck, facing the cold of the January night after the warmth of the bus. Women bustled hurriedly with their bulging shopping bags in their haste to get home in time for their husband's tea. Children made up the madding crowd, half dragged along by their mothers free hand, none too happy with all this rushing and pushing. The old man on the corner of the bus station was selling his evening papers with zest. Some of the football crowd were making a night of their team's victory by making for the pubs as they opened their doors with silent punctuality. Some would drink their pint and leave the pub with a certain amount of pride and satisfaction. Others would drink into their beer with greedy thirst and inwardly scorn what they called the dull man who had just left, leaving only the rebels who secretly pat each other on the back with comradeship that only men could have. And with the drink comes never-ending pride and devotion that these are your friends. Gone are the doubts that you once so bravely pushed aside like the rebel you are. Gone also are the last of the dull, hen-pecked bastards that look so smug as they puff their pipes and slyly look around the bar. Gone too are the worries of work and all that goes with it. The routine has stopped for them.

The long bar was crowded with the football crowd, intermixed with the down-and-outs of the city. I walked towards the bar, feeling the eyes of the few downtrodden bums on me, making me feel like a king amongst beggars, and was I not a king with my own house, my beautiful wife, the gold ring that adorned my finger? The watch on my wrist is wafer thin. But I was a restless king, not quite satisfied with my lot, fascinated by the rest of my kingdom, always a hankering to go back to the peasants. Some strange fascination that brought me back — what am I searching for, what magnetic desire brings me into this rough and most surely ready pub? Something much more than drink, yet it is drink I ask for. As the barman looks with admiration at the smart, well-dressed youth, I look with stirring excitement at the dirty, downtrodden old man in the corner with his grimy beard and tattered coat. He looks my way with watering eyes. What thoughts are passing through your mind, old timer? The beer the barman has brought me is cold to my lips but I drink hungrily into the beer, swilling my young and well-conditioned body, making it warm and so alive. I wink towards the barman and order a double brandy.

He looks at me from crafty eyes, his nose twitching in merriment, turning quickly on spindle legs to splash out the brandy tots. I hand him the money and receive my change, moving over towards the warmth of the fire and the old man. He looks my way slyly. I can feel the room take on a silence. The chatter has changed to murmers. The old man's bony, thin hand trembles, holding his half glass of beer. We stare at each other for a moment then I hand him the brandy. He grasps the glass with greedy hands, a grin comes from his gummy mouth, but I have gone out into the cold of the night to drink more beer like I was meant to do and take away my sadness. But the search still goes on.

The pubs I went into that night are unimportant, the

drinks I consumed are minor details, but it took a lot of drinks to push out of my subconscious the guilt of what I was doing. It was not the guilt of my marriage that caused me concern. It was not the fear of losing my house before I had lived in it. No, it was the dread of my childhood days of losing the only real chance God had given me, but even that was drowned in alcohol, forgetting my fight next week.

* * * * *

"Wake up, luv". Someone was nibbling my ear. I twisted away from the phantom nibbler, doing a nosedive in the blankets but soon coming up for air, my mouth shut tight hiding my furry tongue. But it was my short supply of saliva that made me open my eyes, blinking them around the room.

"How do you feel, luv?", the voice came beside me. I turned towards the woman in the big bed. The very warmth of our bodies in the bed brought back the drowsiness I was feeling. I lay on my side looking at what had once been a very attractive woman, but now she was on the wrong side of forty, wrinkles surrounded her neck, leaving the vital clues that time was no longer her friend. "How did I get here?" I asked, my hand going down to my naked crutch. "Oh, it's a long story, luv. You were in a proper state last night." "Yer", I said through cracked lips. "Do me a favour, will you. Get me a cold drink of water." She jumped out of bed as naked as when she was born, running out of the room, her tits bouncing dutifully in tune with her large buttocks. The bedroom was cosy without much expense — Christ, my money!

My suit was neatly folded on the coat hanger with my sheepskin overcoat hanging on a hook by the door. I searched frantically for my money, my boney knees trembling in the cold bedroom, but there was not even a penny in any of the pockets. Oh Christ, how f--- dumb can you get — me, taken for the three card trick, me, who rolls f--- Yanks, should fall for a move like this. Scouse would have a good f--- laugh if he only knew.

I could hear her coming back up the stairs. I rushed to the big bed. She had put on a housecoat and her hair had been fastened in a pink ribbon, making her face more angelic and much younger. She carried a glass of water. "Here you are", she said, giving me the water, and from the other hand she brought my wallet. "Here you are, Phil." I took the wallet feeling relieved but still wondering how much was inside. She must have read my thoughts. "You have £73 and thirteen bob in silver", she said precisely. "I took £1 out for the taxi", she said, looking straight into my eyes. I nodded in thanks, not caring about the six-and-a-half quid I had not even remembered spending. "How did you know my name?" I asked, wanting suddenly to go to the lavatory. "Oh, I saw it on your boxing licence in your wallet. You were in a terrible state last night, luv. All the time you were shouting and wanting to fight the whole pub. I knew that if I had not got you out, you would have been lying in the gutter with nothing in your pockets," she said kindly. "Then all the way home in the taxi you started crying and telling me that you were not yellow."

"Where is the lav?" I asked, not caring about my nudity. "Oh, down the steps, luv, and then through the scullery out into the yard", she said.

★ ★ ★ ★ ★

"Phil, don't you think you should go home?" Jean asked,

looking at me sadly as we lay side by side in bed. "Do you want me to, Jean?" I said, suddenly raising up and leaning on my elbow. "You know I don't", she replied, a faint smile creasing her face, "but I have noticed you these past few days — you seem restless — why don't you face the music, luv? It's no good running away from it all. Go back to her. She needs you, what with her having the baby." "Carol never needed anybody, Jean," I said bitterly. "Oh Phil, they will all wonder what has happened to you", she concluded.

All the time for the past week I had stayed in bed, drinking the brandy that Jean fetched back from the off-licence. I felt like a prisoner who feels the fear of going out into the world of traffic and people. I was happy in bed drinking my fears away, but they would come back to me in double dosage so that drink was more necessary than ever. I could not face anyone except Jean. She was my contact, my errand boy to the outside world. What had brought this on? I had felt so let down with everything. Nothing seemed important. The fanfares did not come when I got my own house. The handshakes came from strangers, not from my own people. My wife was too correct, too sure. There was no depth in her love – I want too much from my dreams. I have waited too long; I have become impatient. The apples have to be rosy and red without them going through the winters of poverty.

Jean threw the daily paper on the bed as I drank into the brandy. I read into the paper, finding out how they were living outside. "Mystery of Missing Boxer" — I read it twice before I realised I was reading about myself. The words made my belly send butterflies into orbit — "Mystery of Missing Boxer". There was some account of what my manager had said to the promoter, Joe Shepperd in Newcastle, that Phil McGrath would be ready and fit for the fight, saying that I was going to Halifax to see my wife who was staying with her mother. Yes, it was true McGrath had bought his own house in Castleford. Carol McGrath would make no comment. McGrath's mother-in-law said "We don't know where he is, and I'm not in the least bothered."

"Jean, I'm going tomorrow. Here, love, take this", I said, giving her a tenner. "Phil, you have been good to me. I don't need this", she said. "Oh shut up, will yer and get me some brandy." You are doing the right thing, Phil. This is no way of wasting your life, drinking all the time. You are lucky you have got somebody to go home to."

CHAPTER 28

THE FALLEN IDOL

I walked through Halifax like a condemned man. What the hell could I say? I did not even know myself. "Well, it's like this, Carol. I'm sick to the teeth of you and all you stand for, but most of all I'm sick of myself. Nothing is important any more. Oh yes, but there is something I want, Carol, but you will never be able to understand. I would like to see the tears come to your eyes when you see me. But they won't because that would not be correct and that is something you are, correct. Or maybe I would settle for a show of temper — I would know there is feeling."

"Hello Phil",the ginger-headed bus conductor said, clicking out a ticket. "Where yer been hiding yerself?" And I suddenly realised that was just what I had been doing. "I was yellow",I said with sincerity. "Not you, Phil",he laughed, "not you." But he was wrong, I was yellow. Life was my opponent and I just could not face it.

I walked up the garden path to the bungalow. Eyes darted from behind flowery curtains. I rang the door bell unnecessarily. The door was flung open to the white faces of mother and daughter. "What do you want, Phil?", Carol said, hiding behind her mother. "Oh Christ", I wanted to laugh; I wanted to say "Could I have the leg over Carol, please?" "I would like to speak to you on your own, Carol." "Well, she does not want to speak to you, Phil" — the cool voice of her mother. I looked towards Carol and she made a move to go inside to her nice, cosy bungalow. I pushed the two fivers towards her which did more f--- harm than good. "She does not want your money", her mummy said. "No," I thought, "that's the f--- trouble."

★ ★ ★ ★ ★

The Central Area Boxing Board of Control fined me £50 and three months suspension. My manager was fined £200. I felt sick for Jimmy Lumb. I had told the committee that it was all my fault and Mr. Lumb was free of any blame. Mr. Joe Shepperd, the Newcastle promoter, said that I would never fight on any of his bills again.

★ ★ ★ ★ ★

"You better frame yourself and get a job. I'm not having you sulking around here all day", mam said in the kitchen of the prefab. "Just who the hell do you think you are that you can treat everybody like servants? Pack this drinking in and get yourself a job, otherwise you are out," she finished.

I got a job on the dustbins. How happy and contented I really was. Two o'clock would find us drinking in the pub and talking about the fight game. My weight had shot up to ten and a half stone, but in this simple job I felt happy and free from any fear of humiliation. I did not need any brains to empty bins. I was as contented as I had ever been outside my world of boxing. I always had the excuse that I was only doing this dirty-stupid job while my suspension went on, but deep down I enjoyed every minute of working on the dustbins.

There was a bloke on the dustbins called Brer Rabbit because of the prominence of his huge teeth but this *nom-de-plume*, as my mother-in-law would say, would never be mentioned in his presence owing to the fact that Brer Rabbit stood six-feet-four in his stockings and weighed in the region of seventeen stone. Now, it was a well-known fact that Brer Rabbit could not tell the time of day but, for some strange reason, to combat this predicament he carried in his waistcoat pocket a gold Albert watch, so from time to time we would shout "What time do yer make it, Brer Sidney?" He always thought the "Brer" was some German address for Mr. Anyway, he would glance at his gold Albert and proceed to walk towards us to show us the time, but we would walk away, still shouting out "What's the time, Brer Sidney", as if we did not know he couldn't tell the time. So he would be near on chasing us around the dustcart in his endeavour to show us the time. The poor bugger hadn't the sense to say f--- the lot of you, and he was certainly big enough to be able to do it.

But little Percy went too far one Friday teatime. He found some perfume in a big bottle from one of the dustbins, and when Brer Rabbit was bending over, he poured the f--- lot over Brer Rabbit's arse and back. Now, I will admit Brer Rabbit did not smell too good at the best of times, but this was going to the extreme. Summer was not doing any favours as the April sun shone down on our grimy clothes. But I swear there was enough perfume to have covered a thousand whores in a Kowloon brothel. The sickly smell pervaded the air; people passing the dustcart could smell it; straggly tomcats could smell it as they leaped behind the dustbins away from the poisonous smell, but Brer Rabbit, he could smell nothing. He emptied the bins with long years of experience and efficiency. All around him we chuckled and laughed at the spectacle. Tears smarted our eyes and we rubbed dirty hands to our faces to cover without success our laughter. Brer Rabbit caught the bus that night, only to be ejected. The stench on the bus must have been terrible.

That night was the night I 'phoned my manager and was

told I could have my supsension lifted to fight the No. 1 in the world at twelve days' notice, Rafuie King. So I guess I forgot about my working buddies. I was told that Brer Rabbit found out Percy's little joke and promptly threw him in the dustcart, but I don't know how true that is.

But looking back over the years, I realise that the confidence I derived from working on that dustcart was to a certain degree through Brer Rabbit. Here at last was a man who was actually worse than myself. Here at last was a man who took the spotlight off my own inadequacy away from me, and also there was the loophole of being able to say that I was only doing this dirty job while I was suspended. So really I was a no-good, two-faced bastard who was laughing at Brer Rabbit's inadequacy to hide my own.

★ ★ ★ ★ ★

The fight with King brought Carol and myself back together again. I had a daughter now, called Melanie Jane. And once more we set out — but this time together — to Castleford to live. Jimmy took well the incident of my failing to turn up for the fight.

I bought a house for £900. It was not the house of my dreams. It was a street house but it was a start to cash in once again.

With Carol I always get the impression that while I was in the public eye she was attracted to me, but when the chips were down I would not find her around. I had received my share of publicity from my own local paper in Halifax from my fight with King, and I had been paid well — £1,000.

CHAPTER 29

THE WEIGH-IN

Solomons' place was crowded the afternoon of the fight. The blaring loudspeaker was shouting the names of the boxers for the main event — Brian London and Peter Radamacher. I watched tensely as London stripped to his trunks. "All right, Phil?", he said. "Yes, all right, Brian", I replied. He shuffled out of the dressing room, his dressing gown covering his broad shoulders. I could see Solomons standing by the scales waiting for London and Radamacher to appear. The chatter of the cockneys as they took in these two gladiators, and the scent of cigar smoke came back to the dressing room, bringing to you the atmosphere of the occasion. I marvelled as always at the miracle that forever confronted me when at these big fights, that Phil McGrath should be fighting Rafuie King, the number one in the world, the chief support to the big fight. Oh dad, how I wish that you could have been alive to help and inspire me. Just to hear you speak would have been enough to give me the courage to destroy this man. What is this thing I lack, that I should throw away this chance of a lifetime for drink? Would it have been different if you had been alive? You were the only person I ever respected, or is this, too, fate that I will end up like you? I can feel the fear clawing at me this very second. Oh, the mental anguish, the disgust I feel for myself.

McGrath, King — the speaker blares out the names. I quickly strip down to my undershorts as my manager pushes my lambskin coat over my shoulders. I'm bustled down the gangway to the scales. Now and again someone would pat me on the back and wish me the best of luck. King was already at the scales, surrounded by the officials. I took in his moustache as he smiled my way. Jack Solomons shook my hand and enquired my weight. I told him I would be overweight. He smiled, "O.K. Phil." I knew he was not worried with me only being a substitute. King weighed in at 9st. 2lbs. The official shouted, looking around at the few hundred or so people. I moved aside for King to stand off the scales, but he stopped and held his hand out for me to shake. I looked him straight in the eyes, but nothing did I see. This was a good fighter, there was no doubt about that. You could see it in his manner, in every movement. I stood on the scales, knowing I was confronted with a formidable task, but my father was lurking somewhere beyond, daring me to admit my defeatism. McGrath weighing in at 9st. 6lbs. I could hear the murmur of the crowd. My manager was leading me back to the dressing room. Everyone was chattering excitedly. I could see London changing back into his clothes. He winked over my way as he fastened the knot of his tie.

I quickly put on my clothes wanting so much to be away from the tension and atmosphere of the coming fight, but knowing full well that it would follow me out of Solomons' to the restaurant where I would nibble my steak, then back to the hotel to lay on my bed. My manager and I walked into Windmill Street, aware of the crowd jostling to catch a glimpse of the boxers. We walked around the corner, coming out on to the restaurant which we always used when boxing in London. The waiter greeted each of us upon entering. "The usual, please", my manager said, as I took off my overcoat. I scratched my growth of beard nervously as I looked around the restaurant. "Well, Phil, if you can give this boy a good fight, we are in the big time", my manager said, looking over at me. I nodded, not wanting to say anything. He went on, "I know you have only had twelve days to train for the fight, Phil, but you did some training whilst you were suspended, didn't you?", he asked, looking enquiringly at me. "I already told you I have, Jimmy", I lied. The waiter came over with the steaks which filled up the plates. "A glass of orange juice", I said, looking up into his Latin face. I chewed my steak slowly.

"Well, Phil, I can't stress to you the importance of this fight", Jimmy went on. "This boy could get a world title fight any time. There's no doubt he's a good one but he can be roughed up. You can do it, Phil", he said encouragingly. I knew that if I was to spring any surprises it would have to be early on. Oh God, why had I not trained while I was suspended? I thought of the conversation I'd had with Jimmy on the telephone. "I have got you King if you want him, Phil. Don't worry, Solomons got them to lift your suspension". "How much, Jimmy?" I asked. "I've got you a grand." "A what?" I said. "A thousand" Jimmy's voice shouted in the telephone. "Hello, hello, are you still there?" I could hear Jimmy saying in the 'phone, but I was stunned. "Yes", I had suddenly blurted out, "I will fight Joe Lewis for that", but twelve days was not nearly enough for the fight. If only I had trained while I had been suspended, but no, I was too full of my own self-pity, wanting so much for people to help drown my sorrows. But it was no good now, the fight was tonight and nothing could alter that fact.

The steak tasted truly delicious but I just couldn't do it justice. I pushed my plate away, forcing a smile across at Jimmy. "What's the matter, boy, don't you feel up to it?" Jimmy said, looking concernedly across at me. "I had too much at breakfast this morning", I lied. "Well boy, let's be getting back to the hotel", he said, pushing himself up from the table. He called for a taxi and soon we arrived back at our hotel. "Here is the key, Phil", take the lift up to your floor. I will stay down here and let you get some rest", Jimmy stated. The lift boy nodded his greeting at me as I walked into the lift. "Which floor, sir?" he asked. "The sixth, please", I replied, feeling the lift suddenly shoot up from the floor. A shiver or a passing ghost passed through my body. I stood transfixed. In my thoughts I experienced once more the wonderment of the predicament I found myself in. Was I really fighting this world-rated opponent? Was it really true that the people at Jack Solomons' were shaking my hand and looking at me with respect? How much am I in your debt, dad, for gaining all these people's respect, and you're not here, dad, to see your son fighting. But your spirit will always be near me in the ring. I will never ever let you down, dad. I feal the fear, but it's the fear that I could ever let you down. "Sixth floor, sir", the boy said, smiling into my face. I passed down the passage with its blood-red carpets, making you feel guilty as though you were walking in a bath of blood. Yes, dad, we have come a long way, yet still I feel so insecure. Will this doubting feeling go on for ever?

I prodded the key into the door and walked into the luxury of the room. I glanced around, smiling at my own thoughts of days gone by. If that teacher could see me, the one who looked at me as if I were something the cat dragged in, oh, how I wish you too could see me now, lazy eye. How you took delight in humiliating me. I undressed quickly and slid between the cold sheets. It was impossible to sleep but I was resting. Oh dad, give me strength. I searched for every word he had ever said to me, drawing from them a confidence. How quickly you died, showing no fear. How can I ever be scared of any man when you have shown me by your own deeds that it was all in the mind? But I do show fear, dad. I really am scared. I am not fit for this fight, what must I do? Yes, I know what you would have told me to do. Fight until you drop. Why am I worrying? No-one can hurt me like you hurt me. Remember our Topsy — I swore that no-one would ever do that to me. I must try to sleep. I could feel the heat of my body. I pushed the blankets from me and jumped out of bed. I shadow boxed, throwing punches lightly in the air. I stopped and sat on my bed. I could hear the clock on the table ticking over. 2.30, but how slow it's going!

I walked into the bathroom and swilled my face, looking into the mirror and noticing how flat my nose was getting. The scar tissue of my left eye hung slack over the lid. I could see the tension in my eyes, wanting desperately for the fight time to arrive and dreading the waiting. I threw the towel over the side of the bath, impatient at this waiting game. I must get a grip. O.K. so I hadn't trained. I was a substitute, but they were paying me good money for this fight. I must be in with a chance. They had tried Terry Spinks, but he didn't want King. I couldn't afford to choose who I wanted or who I didn't want. I was a hungry northerner who had to be thankful for small mercies from the London crowd. Solomons had given me a chance, so it was up to me to take it. I went back to bed, sinking into the warmth of the sheets. I closed my eyes, forcing all thoughts of the fight from me, and drowsed into a fitful sleep.

I could hear a light knocking on the door. I awoke instantly from my unsettled sleep. Jimmy came through to my room. "How do you feel, Phil?" he asked, holding a couple of oranges in his hand. "I've got a couple of Jaffas for you to suck on after the fight, lad", he stated cheerfully. I glanced at the clock, ticking the minutes away. 10 past 6. Gosh, I must have slept. I felt proud with myself. "I'll ring for a couple of poached eggs on toast", Jimmy said, grabbing hold of the 'phone. "Okay, Jimmy", I agreed, feeling happy that the waiting was nearly over. I buttoned up my trousers and went into the bathroom, dousing cold water all over my face. I had sensed the excitement in Jimmy as soon as he walked through the door. Yes, it was a big night for both of us. He had been like a father to me, even when I had been suspended he had stuck by me. I shuffled into the room as Jimmy was putting the bandages and tapes into my bag. There came a light knock on the door, and the bell boy entered with the toast and eggs set out on a tray. I watched him fluttering round the table, then I sat down and hungrily set about the food. Jimmy was busy checking my medical case, making sure we had got everything. "Listen, Phil", Jimmy stated, "if it happens, mind you, I only say if, well, if you are having a tough time out there", he went on quietly, "I will throw the towel in." "No, Jimmy, you must promise me here and now that you will never do that." "Well listen, Phil, it will be no disgrace losing to this boy." "I don't care, Jimmy. I want you to promise me you will not throw in the towel." "All right then", he said, shrugging his shoulders.

CHAPTER 30

THE HOUR OF MEDITATION

I walked through the turnstiles, Jimmy close behind me carrying my bag. The man nodded as Jimmy spoke my name. We walked close together, as people stopped to stare at us, noticing Jimmy with my bag. The pool was only half full but it still was a frightening sight. We turned off to go to the dressing room, a corridor of rooms. I noticed London's name stuck on the door with adhesive tape. I could feel the churning in my stomach, the mental torment within me. All around us people were rushing to and fro; a man carrying his boxer's boots and gloves passed us by. "Here we are", Jimmy said, standing outside the dressing room door. I stood there, taking in my name, Phil McGrath. How proud I was. I stopped as I saw the tape had come loose, and fastened it back down with my hand, pressing gently, my palm across my name. Jimmy proceeded in getting my things out of the bag, and folding my towel and dressing gown over the chair. I lay on the big table, using my overcoat as a pillow. I could hear the W.H.I.P. outside, noisily getting the six-round supporting contest ready. Jimmy was snipping the tape, and sticking it neatly on the wall. I watched him, sensing the excitement within him. He looked over at me and winked. I smiled back, hiding my nervousness.

"Well, Phil boy, we have roughly one hour before we go on", he said, looking down at his watch. "We are on the first fight after the interval. London's fight is one after you", he continued, "we might as well take our time and tape your hands nice and easy." I sat up from the table, my legs dangling over the side. He came over with the bandage, and proceeded bandaging my hands, stopping now and again for me to clench and test the comfort. He worked methodically, not taking his eyes from my hand except to take a piece of tape from the wall. "How does that feel, Phil?", he asked, looking down at the finished fist. I could hear the M.C. announcing the first fight. I clenched and unclenched my right hand. "That's O.K., Jimmy", I replied. "All right, try it on my hand", he said, holding the palm of his right hand up to the side of him. I stood clenching my fist and gave his hand a couple of wacks. "Wow, if you hit him like that, Phil boy, to-night you'll stiffen him", Jimmy said, grinning at me. I could hear the boxers' names being shouted down the corridor. Now and again someone would put his head round the door and wish me luck.

I sat on the chair as Jimmy started on my left hand. So as my time approached, like the condemned man waiting in his cell, I went back to the one person in my hour of need, my father, my saviour. I remembered an incident when I was 14, just boys, waiting in the dressing room, each of us feeling the strain of waiting to go into the ring. My dad had spotted my opponent going into the lavatory. "Get in there after him", he said, nodding towards the lavatory. "After who?" I asked, innocently. "The bugger you're fighting, you dope. Just give him a couple of backhanders." I walked nervously towards the lavatory, obeying dad's every command. I grabbed the boy by the scruff of the neck and slapped his face with my open hand. "You're fighting me", I said, delighted at the fear he was showing. I walked out of the lavatory feeling so pleased with myself. "Alright", dad stated proudly. I smiled at my thoughts of this man. What tricks would you be up to tonight, dad?

The interval was approaching. The W.H.I.P. burst open the door. "O.K. Phil, start getting ready", he said, the sweat trickling down his forehead. Jimmy was slashing the soles of my new boxing boots so as to prevent me slipping to the canvas. "Here, lace this one up", he said, passing me the boot with the brand new laces. No, I'm not going down on any canvas tonight, dad; I'll show him how we fight down Woolshops. I stripped to my trunks, putting on my leather protector, making sure my straps were not twisted round my buttocks. Jimmy gave me the other boot and I started pulling them on, lacing them not quite to the top. I slipped on my green satin shorts, sliding them over my protector.

I could feel the sweat coming from within my bandaged hands. The fear was gripping me once again. What right had I to be here tonight, fighting this great little fighter, who was based in Paris but came from darkest Africa? Had I not thought of the danger that could befall me when I agreed to go in with him at twelve days notice? Solomons had tried all the top-rated Londoners but they did not want him, but you said yes, I will fight King Kong for that. Yes, but that was twelve days ago and look at me now. Oh, the fear that passes through me as I wait for the W.H.I.P. to shout my name. Why should I always resort to playing the hero, then afterwards go through the agonies of a coward? Phil McGrath is fighting Rafuie King who's in the world ratings, and I saw him in the pub pissed as a newt last week, people of Halifax were saying. And you thought it was all so adventurous and exciting for people to talk this way about you. But now I'm scared and I need you, dad, to help me. What must I do, please tell me, dad? I could feel his steady eyes piercing through me. Get off your arse, you yellow little sod. Is that you talking to me, dad, can it really be you? Yes, it's me, and I'm sick of the sight of you, always wanting me to come to your rescue, as you sit on your arse cringing. I stood up, feeling the anger at my own thoughts. Yes, I am sick to the teeth of you. You blamed me for nearly killing a bloke in Hong Kong, but you knew you were too good for him. So you played the cat and mouse game with him. Now the chips are turned around. You are the mouse and King's the cat. Go in that ring and make your mother proud of you.

I shadow boxed, feeling the inspiration flooding my body, the longing to be in the ring and hit out at the anger and pent-up frustration I felt within myself. Jimmy came over with the jar of vaseline, waiting patiently for me to finish shadow boxing. I stopped abruptly, the hatred for the incompleteness I felt for myself subsiding. I felt the coldness of the vaseline as Jimmy fingered it on my eyebrows, then smeared some on the side of my ribs. We grinned at each other, knowing the excitement we both felt. "How are you, my boy?" Jimmy asked, looking into my eyes. "I'm O.K.", I said, feeling relieved that the waiting was nearly over. The W.H.I.P. ducked his head past the door. "Three minutes, the last round just coming up", he stated, holding his three fingers up in front of him. I fidgeted nervously as Jimmy helped me on with my dressing gown. "Take your time, son", Jimmy said, as I fumbled for the hole in the sleeve of the gown. I could feel the heat coming from my face as I jerked the hood of my gown over my head. I had a sudden impulse to scream out against the fear that gripped into my every sinew. Dad, where are you, my subconscious was saying. Steady boy, calm down, remember he's scared too, I could hear him saying. Don't let this kid lick you before you get into the ring, Phil. The W.H.I.P. came hurrying through the door. "O.K. Phil, you're on now." I stood, feeling a calmness pass over my body. "All right, dad", I heard myself say, "this is the big time."

Jimmy had his arm around my shoulder, steadying me

down the gangway of the vast Wembley Pool. My eyes were darting nervously to people who wished me luck. I could see, amidst the ocean of faces, the bright lights encircling above the ring, and the tobacco smoke lingering like a ghost from another world. I felt a shiver run down my spine, making me encounter a terrible loneliness. I wanted so much to turn my back away from the ring and hide myself far away from all this. But what was it I feared more than King, that forever persecuted my subconscious? This obsession I had to be somebody, yearning always to be in the limelight, and my dad knew this. I walked up the steps leading into the ring, noting well-known personalities as they stared at me, "Phil McGrath", in awe. I watched them pulling on their cigars. I could see Peter Wilson staring up at me. King was already in the ring, doing a jig in his corner. He nonchalantly looked across at me as his second helped him off with his gown.

I felt calmness spreading through my body, relieved that the time had now arrived. The referee came across to my corner and asked for a towel, proceeding to wipe off the vaseline from my eyebrows. He smiled and walked away. I rubbed my feet in the box of resin, looking out into the darkness of Wembley Pool. How the hell did I ever get here? What suicidal madness should bring me here tonight? And yet there was no panic in my thoughts. It was as if someone was holding in my fear, gently telling me, what is there to life, what is there to death? But it is because of life that I am here. I am so scared of life, trying in vain to find the weakness of my inadequacies. I have proved to myself that I fear no man by standing in this corner waiting to fight this world-rated opponent. Well then, what is it I fear?

The light dimmed low. "Ladies and gentlemen, this is a ten-round contest, three minutes each round." Jimmy had his hand resting lightly on my shoulders. "Watch your step,

Phil, the first round. Don't let him con you into any false moves", he said. But I was back down Woolshops with my little friend, Terry O'Brian. You're yellow, I could hear myself saying. No, you're not, Terry's voice came through my subconscious. Well, come on then, let's go over the other side of the roof of the copper works.

CHAPTER 31

THE SHOW DOWN

"At the weighing to-day, King weighed 9st. 2lbs, McGrath 9st. 6lbs. Your timekeeper, Mr. Joe..." I could feel the impatience within me listening to the formalities of the introduction. I turned around and looked across at King as he danced to his own silent music. The referee motioned each of us to the centre of the ring. I stared at King's goodlooking profile. He looked like a miniature Sugar Ray. He stared back at me, seemingly inspecting my face, looking for any scar tissue that his fists could work on with surgeon-like precision. I smiled at him, admiring his act, but intent not to give him the upper hand of this psychological game. I knew in myself that I could beat this man if we were to fight in a locked lavatory, but that was not to be. We were fighting here in the vastness of the ring, but all the same it still gave me a psychological advantage before the fight. I speared my eyes at him and sneered at him with all the contempt I could muster. He smiled back at me, his white teeth flashing, knowing the game we each were playing. "Right boys", the referee was saying, "I want you to give me a good clean fight, no holding or butting, when I say break, I want you to break straight away." We both nodded, acknowledging what he was saying but hardly listening to his words, eager to be on with the fight. "Well, let's have a good fight from both of you, best of luck."

We touched gloves and walked back to our respective

corners to await the bell sounding out the first round. Jimmy held the gumshield out ready for me. I opened my mouth to receive it. "Good luck boy", Jimmy said, as the bell sounded for the first round. King appeared like a genie in front of me, as if Aladdin had rubbed his magic lamp. I felt a relief pass through my body, thankful that the fight had started. King flicked a light left into my face which I blocked and countered to the belly. But King never stayed in one place too long. I shook him with a right to the body. He acknowledged my point with a smile, but behind the smile came two lightning left hand punches that rocked my head back with the sheer speed and power of their delivery. I felt the panic let loose inside of me. He sensed my desperation as he sent my way a volley of punches from all angles. I ducked and weaved in haste to be free of this relentless attack, but still his punches came upon me with deadly accuracy, and then it seemed the inner hatred and bitterness, the resentment that lay dormant was coming to the surface. How dare this nigger humiliate me in front of thousands of people. I made a promise that no man would humiliate me.

I stood toe to toe with King, punching with all the venom my arms could allow. I could feel him grunt. This was how I like to fight, seeing my opponent in front of me. But very soon he fluttered away like the butterfly he was, leaving only the breeze of my punches to indicate how dangerous this butterfly was. I walked towards King, inspiration spreading through my body, but King was there once more with his lightning punches to remind his pupil that the master was still in the room. The bell tolled out its message that a well-earned rest was waiting. I stared at King with somewhat disappointment as he danced back to his corner. Jimmy was waiting in my corner with a look of relief on his face. I sat heavily on the stool, feeling the coldness of the sponge. I half listened to the words Jimmy was saying. "You must crowd him, Phil, before he gets on his bike." I knew what he meant. I must make him stand and fight. But how do you tell a butterfly to come into your net? I could feel the swell of my left eye as the sponge splashed across my face.

The bell sounded for the next round. I pushed the gumshield into my mouth and rushed to the centre of the ring, hinting in my eagerness that we must fight it out, but King jabbed out punches and moved out of range. Now and again a volley of punches would jolt into my head, sending it back, so that tears of frustration would blur my eyes, wanting so much to trap him in a corner and butt and gouge, and have done with the fencing and humiliation I was going through. Yet there he was in front of me, happy in the knowledge that he'd found the key to my end but probing, wary, like the matador waiting for the bull to make its rush. My left eye was completely shut as King probed without mercy his spear-like lefts. I stood bemused in the centre of the ring, feeling once more the humiliation at not finding the answer to this man's speed of foot and razor-sharp reflexes that sent my head rocking on my shoulders. But with the humiliation came the anger as always, to bring out my hatred for myself, for my inadequacy to cope with my world outside the ring. Never before had it entered my world of boxing, but now it was here in front of me, prodding into ruins my secure world of boxing.

Yet what must I do to stop this man who unknowingly was taking away the last grain of confidence I possessed. I rustled him to a corner, throwing punches wildly his way. Blood was dripping freely from my left eye. I could see over King's shoulder Tommy Farr at the ringside, motioning with his fists for me to work to the body. I sent a burst into King's body, but more to please Farr than my own satisfaction. My stamina was waning. Once more King was backpedalling, but leaving behind the destruction and savageness of his punches. My left eye was shut tight, making me stand square on to be able to get any view of this black flash, and him knowing the desperation I was going through, he bided his time, not wanting to end the enjoyment he was having with the trapped animal, and knowing full well the desperation of the very same animal. Nothing must be left to chance. So this was my punishment for all the wrongs I had done. Had I not done the same to the Chinese boy as King was doing to me? I heard the welcome sound of the bell.

As King nonchalantly walked to his corner, I had a sudden urge to leap at him and butt and kick him in the balls, wanting so much to even the score with this great little fighter. I restrained myself, grinning at my own thoughts. Jimmy was looking worriedly at me as he removed my gumshield. "How's it go, Phil?", Jimmy asked, using the swab to stop the trickle of blood coming from my left eye. "Not so good, Jim", I mumbled from my bruised lips. "Does he punch real hard, kid?" "He punches hard, Jim, but no K.O. punch", I said. I wished to Christ he had, I thought. "Well, listen, son, I am going to stop the fight if you don't frame yourself." "Fuck to you", I said, as the bell sounded for the third round. King was already waiting for me as I reluctantly walked towards the centre of the ring, and so it went on, the taunting of the red cape by the Matador and the desperation and rushes of the bull. I hooked King a good one to the body just to remind him that I was still in with a chance, but suddenly he retaliated with punches coming from all angles. I watched my gumshield zip through the air, not believing that it had once fitted my mouth snugly. The reflexes of this man were so fast that every punch I threw his way he countered with split second timing, making me reluctant to throw out any punches at all. And so it went on, this one-sided battle, until the fifth round. The referee wrapped his arms around me and led me back to my corner. I protested half-heartedly, feeling in some way I had to do this out of respect to my father. Jimmy was pulling at my gloves, relief written all over his face. I smiled at him as he ruffled my hair. My dad had told me never to be proud of being a loser, and here I was beaming with relief and pride at taking a beating. I wonder what you would say to these thoughts I am having at this moment? I walked into my lonely dressing room, Jimmy silently shutting the door. I sat on the chair, vaguely staring around the room. Was it all worth the bother to have people's respect. Was my journey really necessary?

CHAPTER 32

THE CHANCE ENCOUNTER

Jimmy had tried to talk me out of going to any night club, but I had stubbornly told him I was going, so I had jumped in a taxi, telling him I would see him at Windmill Street the following morning. I slipped the dark glasses over my eyes, squinting into the darkness of the cab, wanting so much for the car to fly like an aeroplane over each set of traffic lights and the busy London traffic, and to descend like a helicopter outside the Ambassador nightclub. "Where to, guv?", the driver interrupted my thoughts. "The Ambassador, please", I said, leaning back in the seat. I licked my bruised lips, feeling the puffiness of my upper lip. "You been to the fights, guv?" my driver asked. "Yes, I was there", I said, thinking that was as good a reply as I could give. "How did Brian London make out?" he asked. "Oh, he won well" I replied. "Yea", the driver inclined his head, looking through the mirror at me. "You ain't been fighting too, have you, guv?" "You might say I have helped out", I said, disgustedly. "Who did you fight?" the driver asked, half turning in the driver's seat. "I think I fought one of those Aussie kangaroos", I laughed.

"What they call you, guv?" "Phil McGrath." "Christ, you fought the coon — what's his name?" "Rafuie King", I replied. "Yes, that's the boy", the driver went on. "Some fighter, that kid. I think he'll get a shot at the world title." I nodded my head in agreement. The taxi came to a halt outside the club door. I fumbled in my pocket and brought out a pound note. "Thanks, guv", I said, mocking the Londoner as I made my way to the entrance of the club. I pushed another pound note into the doorman's hand as he smiled falsely at me, beckoning me to go through. A blonde was screeching out words of love into the mike, a shimmering green satin dress clearly showing the contours of her body. I could feel the tension of my early hours of mental and physical strain relaxing, bringing a carefreeness within myself. The waiter was upon me before I sat myself at the table. I felt the wildness and recklessness of my nature. "I want a bottle of champagne", barking my order with an air of authority. He nodded, giving me a sly look.

I sat back in my seat, taking in the blonde's act, her diddies jumping out of her dress in their haste to become naked once more. I felt a yearning for a grind. The waiter came back with the champagne in a green, decorated bucket. I smiled, waving my hand to tell him to be gone and leave me to the pouring. I drank greedily of the champagne, feeling the smarting of my cut lips. I belched into the glass, smiling to myself at my ignorance. The hostess looked my way invitingly as I peered through my glasses. I poured another drink and waved her across with my glass. "Hello darling, do you want me?" she said as she planted herself down next to me. "Yes", I said, "I want you so badly that I'm going to phone my daddy who owns a mill in Halifax, and tell him I'll be coming home with a brand new bride." She giggled, "Oh you are a one, you are", as if she was a virgin in a convent. I smiled as if pleased with her remark.

Taking in the dark shadows under her eyes, I nonchalantly pulled the wad of notes out of my pocket and waved the waiter over for some more champagne. She looked disinterestedly at the notes as I handed them to the waiter. We smiled at each other as we drank of the champagne. "Your father hasn't got a mill, has he?" she asked, grinning over at me. "No", I said, keeping my face straight, "but mam used to work in one." We both laughed at the remark. "What's up with your eyes?" she asked. "I'm a peeping Tom", I said, lifting the glasses up from my eyes. "Stop joking and tell me", she said, smiling at me. "All right", I said, "if you promise to sleep with me." "Oh, you are a cheeky one, you are", she giggled. "I thought you northerners are supposed to be slow", she said. "Listen, love, if you'd seen me earlier tonight, you would have said I was bloody slow", I stated. The champagne was making my head spin.

"Excuse me", the dark skinned stranger said, looking down into my face, "but would you mind removing your glasses." "What?", I exploded, jumping to my feet. I stood staring stupidly up into his face. "And who the bloody hell are you to tell me to take my glasses off?" I hiccupped. "Listen, wack, don't you know who I am? Remember the chickens, wack?" "Who's chicken?" I said, grabbing hold of his lapel. "Where yer going?" I whined to the blonde as she hurried away, ignoring my drunkenness. "You always like long, black-haired birds, wack." "Yes, that's true. Say, how the hell did you know that?" I said. "Because I was there when you laid that one in Kowloon. It's your old pal, Scouse." I stared at his thick lower lip. "Christ, it can't be Scouse, you no-good, half-chat", I shouted, grabbing hold of him. We embraced each other like Russian premiers.

Drinks came and we drank to the time we had had together — every conversation would start "you remember...;" every hidden memory of it would bring with it a piece of sadness. I felt the tears come to my eyes for the times we had, forgetting the misery we had each endured.

But alas, something was missing, something that told each of us that those days were over for good. My own sensitivity was seeing things that I didn't want to see. I saw the nervousness of Scouse as he secretly glanced at his watch. I saw the silver streaks of his once sleek, black hair. "So you got yourself spliced", I said. "Yes, I married that girl who was writing to me as a pen friend when we was out there. Well, listen wack, I would just like to say how good it has been to have met you once again, and best of luck with your boxing." He got up from the table, looking nervously at his watch. "Are you sure you don't want another drink?" I asked, slurring my words out. "No wack, I must be going. Good luck," he said, shaking my hand.

I watched him passing the people on the floor dancing, and then he was lost forever. What had he said when he was out there? Had he forgotten so easily the times we had — the coke truck, the fights with the M.P.s? Or is it myself who is jealous of Scouse's contentment? What am I searching for, why can't I settle down, why this terrible insecure feeling clawing at me all the time? Waiter, another bottle of champagne. To hell with Scouse, to hell with all you dull bastards.

CHAPTER 33

DOWN AND OUT

I walked about the town centre. Now and again a young couple would casually pass me by, chattering excitedly, and the man would fumble for his money in his haste to be in the pictures in good time for the first house. I watched, feeling the sadness and loneliness pass through my body. I tugged at my collar of my raincoat, conscious of the soiled collar of my shirt. I could feel the sweating of my right hand in which I gripped the two half crowns tightly. I could hear the Salvation Army band striking up its first hymn of the evening on this damp, depressing Sunday. But somehow I felt a comfort whilst listening to the congregation which opened up with "Lead me, O Thou Great Jehova." I could feel the sincerity in their voices as they sang in praise of this great Saviour of men. "Pilgrim in this barren land." People stood gazing across at the group of God's soldiers.

I saw some grinning and joking happily secure in their own existence, but no laughter did I feel, because I would be sharing their hospitality that night, that is, if I had the good fortune to tap a dollar from someone, and no doubt that would not be so very hard. I found that people were very quick to give Phil McGrath a drink or a dollar just to have rid of him, but getting the offer of a bed for the night, that was a different kettle of fish. A couple crossed the road towards me. I recognised the man who had once gone to the same school as me. I fidgeted embarrassedly, not wanting him to see me in the condition I was in. But I need not have worried. He glanced my way and, at the same time jerking his true love's arm, veered some distance above me. I pretended that I hadn't noticed the incident. I smiled but not for long. The contempt I felt for these people lingered within me. I will remember that, my friend. I memorised the day, the hour, and one day Phil McGrath will once more become somebody.

What is it that makes a man a bum? Is it drink? Yes, of course, it was drink, but not altogether. I could never cut a man down in the street like that young upstart had just done. Was this not also one of my own weaknesses? Have you not in some way been compelled to turn your head away from people like me, to further your advancement in your artificial world of falseness. When the drunks came up to me and begged me for drinks, what should I have done? Walk away, and leave them to their own devices? Why did I see the reflection of myself in every down-and-out? This was the constant feeling I experienced whenever I encountered them. Was it because I sensed that I would one day be one of them myself? So, in point of fact, it was my acceptance and giving and not turning my head away which mixed me with the cocktails of alcoholics, which was my downfall. Should I not have been false, and acted the part of a modest person when people would ask me how I would go on in my next fight? Should I not have lowered my head sheepishly and murmered "I really don't know. It's going to be a very hard fight." But that wouldn't have been the true me. How could I ever be timid and false, when my father's cruel and direct attitudes are implanted so deeply inside my every act?

So now that the wheel of fortune has spun against me, leaving me so helpless and insecure, what must I do to combat these cruel people? I must not show them that I am beaten because then the vultures would appear to peck at my corpse, to enjoy every morsel of my failures, to peck away to their friends how Phil McGrath had begged a drink from them! But how do you kid these people on with a dirty shirt and a down-and-out appearance, and shoes that squeak with sogginess and dampness of the wet pavement? Had I not tried to work in this town, the very town where I was born? And to no avail. They utter always a well-coined phrase, "Sorry, you're unsuitable", as soon as my name is mentioned. I know I must give up drinking, but please God tell me how! Without it I could never face the crowd of vultures.

Oh, how I hate myself waking up in derelict houses, reeking of my own drinking sweat, shivering from the cold, hunger and loneliness of my own predicament, often wishing I could be a dull, little man who did not have to be a hero of the town, who works as good as the next man, and at home with a wife fussing around him, always making sure his slippers were warm for him to slip on. What makes me call him a dull little man? When nobody can be as dull or miserable as I am at this minute. Yes, I am jealous of this little man with his slippers and wife, but I had all these things and I threw them all away for this horrid existence. Where will it all end? I am not as strong as my father, nor have I the woman he had. Oh God, hasten and open the doors of the pub and let me forget my worries. Open the doors that bring me the courage, the confidence that I need to fight them. I know that they will still be there again in the morning, but to hell with the morning. I need my drink now, desperately.

The Salvation Army man was shaking the money box in front of me. I spun towards him petrified by his existence and presence. I shook my head at him, disgustingly embarrassed as people gazed my way. I urgently wanted to be away from his company, but not daring to move too quickly for fear of showing my embarrassment, I walked silently away, feeling the relief take over me. I dare not turn around as I could feel the people's eyes upon me. I chuckled to myself craftily at my toughness in refusing the Salvation Army money, forgetting the panic that confronted me when he shook his box in front of my face. Perhaps I should have shook my head in times gone by. I felt terribly sad once more at the pathetic thoughts I was having. Well, sod to the Salvation Army, I only had a dollar, they can't have that.

I walked into the pub, rubbing the stubbly growth on my chin and feeling uneasy but not wanting to show it. "Pint of best, please", I said in my most confident voice. I watched the barman pumping the beer into the glass. My hand was shaking as I handed over my half crown, but nothing could stop my shivers. The barman read into my thoughts as a faint grin creased his face at my dire condition. How quick my own sensitivity was, noting with cleverness of mind, even in pathetic circumstances as I was, the reaction of these people. It was as if "I" was a rich and responsible man going out for a night to act the part of a tramp, a bum, watchfully taking in people's reactions towards myself, and I, fascinated in my hobby masquerading as a bum, but inwardly smiling at these people who tried without success to hide the delight they were experiencing at seeing me in this poor condition. But upon waking in the morning, there would be no transformation of the Cinderella man of the night before, so knowingly my nightmare would begin each day on waking.

I was brought back into the world of reality by the barman speaking, "How are you going on then, McGrath?" It seemed as if he were talking to the whole room of faces, and so the faces looked from him to me, then back once more to the barman as he waited for my reply. So you want to play to the crowd, my friend, I thought. So it shall be. I drank into my pint, licking the wet from my lips. He watched my every movement. I could see the confidence drain from his face, leaving nothing but uncertainty in his eyes. The grin was still there but slowly submerging as if in a sea, and desperately wanting help, but he was doomed to lose. As I knew, good citizens never get involved. He had asked me how I was getting on, and yet he should have known by my appearance that it was a futile question. He had wanted to impress the crowd by mentioning my name — McGrath — and, in the same instance, he was making out that really he couldn't care less for me, the downtrodden being, who had snatched an old lady's handbag, but I could see the unsureness in his actions, the uncertainty in his own courage, and not knowing whether he had sufficient to carry him through.

I could feel his helplessness whilst he glanced for support from his flock of customers who were too intent at drinking into their pints with haste, not wanting to become involved in his act because that is what it was, a poor act. The crowd was his audience, embarrassed and tense, awaiting the next lines to be spoken. Did they think I had not prepared myself for this moment, whilst I lay on my prison bed. "What did you say?" I snapped, but I kept my voice under control. My eyes, the eyes of my father, glared with hatred. I was fully aware of the atmosphere which engulfed the room but my eyes never left the barman. Somehow he plucked up some courage and began again. "I asked you how you were getting on," he stammered with little assurance in his voice. The confidence had very nearly drained completely out of him.

"Yes, I heard you, but I also heard you call me

McGrath, but let me tell you this", I went on, but talking not entirely to him but also for the benefit of everyone present. "You all know undoubtedly where I have been, you all know what I was sent down for. But I have paid my debt, so if there is anyone here who wishes to insult me further, well, here I am, go ahead." I looked around the bar, challenging every face I encountered. I smiled as I drank into my beer. No, I thought to myself, as much as you would like to say something, you would rather wait until my back was turned.

I felt as if I wanted to vomit. I pushed my empty glass on to the counter and walked out. I shivered as I felt the cold, bitter dampness of the night air. God, this was no way to get drunk, I thought. I must make good my next port of call. My hand tightened on the remaining half-crown, and searching frantically for the sixpence that lay hidden in the lining of my pocket, I decided that this wasn't a very good position to be in. I would have to make good at my next pub and make it count. I sauntered to the bottom end of town, getting nearer to Woolshops where I was born, but everything had changed now. The house where I was born no longer stood. Nelson Street was gone, leaving only its memories of so long ago. I stood on the car park with its white lines spaced for each car, and measuring off where our house had once stood.

I walked about in the square parking lot. Yes, here was where our house had stood in this little space. Here was where I had been born. With many thoughts of yesteryears flooding and fleeting in my subconsciousness, with their eagerness to pronounce once more my childhood, I stood still on the tarmacadam looking about me, remembering that where I stood now once stood stone flags, where my mother toiled and scrubbed with her hair falling into her eyes, which seemed to make little difference, unless maybe it made her feel better in herself with her daily chore. I walked to the end of the spaced lot. This, I thought, must have been where our two steps had stood, and there again the sadness came once more, engulfing me deeper with sorrow.

CHAPTER 34

THE INSIGHT OF A BUM

I could hear my ghostly voice being spoken from the past, as I exclaimed: "I am fighting in the school-boy championships, mam! I have put my name down," I whispered. Even then I could see her big brown eyes glaring at me, "Don't talk to me about your boxing! Phil, you know I don't like it, and never will. Nothing ever came of people who fight." I could feel the tears stinging my eyes. Oh mam, how do I get out of this rut? I have thrown away the gift that God gave me.I'm so scared and insecure. I lack the confidence. Where can I go for help? They do nothing but turn away from me. I need someone like my father who will give me the incentive to go on. Why did he have to die so young? I needed him to guide me. He was the only person I would listen to. God, I must get a grip of myself, I thought, and I hurriedly moved away from the car park, wanting so much to get stinking drunk. I entered the pub which was crowded with bums and deadbeats. "Hiya, Phil," the town whore shouted my way. "Do you want a pint?" Ronnie said, beckoning me to the bar where he stood. "I sure do," I shouted, looking cheerfully at him.

"Where have you been all my life?" I shouted across at the Irish bird. She smiled across... not bad, I thought. Ronnie handed me the pint. "What's the crack with that bird over there?" I asked, nodding towards the Irish bird. "I don't rightly know, Phil. She's just moved into Halifax. She's up from the smoke." How yer fixed, Ron?" I asked, looking sorrowfully into his face. "You can have ten shillings, Phil, and I will get your beer in for you," he said, giving me the ten bob. "Thanks, Ron," I said, "you're a good 'un," gaining confidence, knowing that I would once more be able to get drunk again that night. "Where are you kipping, Phil?" Ron asked, looking at my shabbiness. "Oh, I have got a nice little hideout," I replied. "You know you could kip at my place, but for Kath," he said. "Forget it, Ron, it's O.K." "Phil, you have been a bloody fool to yourself," Ron stated. "Oh, don't start that lecturing again, Ron. Let it be." "I'm sorry, Phil, but it makes me mad knowing you have spent your money all over the town, and where are your mates now?"

"You're my mate, aren't you, Ron?" I said, and feeling the beer warming inside me. "You could have made it, Phil," he went on, ignoring my remark. "Oh, for Christ's sake, Ronnie, knock it off. I don't need a sermon from you," I shouted. He looked at me, startled by my outburst. "I'm sorry, old pal, forget it," I said. The beer flowed, making me want to stay forever as I was at that moment. "Phil, I've got to go now. Kath, you know." "Sure, my old pal, and thanks a lot," I said into Ron's ear. He pushed a further dollar into my hand. "Thank you, old pal," I said again, playfully tapping him on the chin. "God bless," I whined as he went for the door. I craftily pushed the money into my pocket. I could see the Irish bird looking my way. I made my way over to her table.

"Hello, my love," I said. "Do you know I am falling in love with you." She smiled at that remark, showing her nice white teeth. "I bet you say that to them all," she said. I loved the Irish lilt of her voice. "I swear to God I don't," I said grinning into her blue eyes. "You are the boxer, are you not?" "And which boxer would that be, my fair colleen?" I said, sitting down beside her. "The one who keeps getting into trouble fighting and what have you," she said. Thank God, I thought, she hadn't mentioned the snatch. "Whereabouts in London are you living," I asked, changing the subject. "Who told you I was down in London?" she replied. "Oh, a little bird. Why what's wrong with that, were you on the game?" I smiled into her face. She cracked me a good one in the mouth, the beer spilling over me. "Don't you ever say that again, McGrath" she said, her eyes glaring at me. "I'm sorry, most girls that come in this pub are on the batter," I replied. "Can I get you a drink?" I asked. "No thanks, I'm only waiting for my sister, she'll be back in a minute," she said. Her sister came back. "I will see you again sometime," I shouted. "Not if I can help it, me boy," she replied.

Drunk and staggering down the still cobbled streets of Woolshops. That very same Woolshops I hated as a small boy, yet now I feel such a warmth and comfort towards you. And pride is also chained together with a deep love that only a drunk can link together in his befuddled imagination. Sadness is there also but oh so faint and gentle like an Angel fleeting past you, murmering sweet nothings in your ear, but never far away, and here she is again reminding me that little girls skipped rope in bare feet, or played hop-scotch in their mother's shoes. But, alas where are you now? You children of my Woolshop days. Are you part of the same people, that have judged me behind your neat lace curtains. Have you turned traitor to the life we once shared? Are you rushing over hills and dales in your fast cars? Forgetting the love we had for each other in the days gone by. Maybe you are holding your own in the 'Rat-race' but I want no part of it — I'm sick of the sight of the 'Phonies'. The truth is what I am searching for, truth to myself. I feel only hate or love — the in-between is pretending. I want so much to give people the very best I have got — and that can only be truth — and what do I get? Hypocritical lies. Here where I was born a car park stands so wastefully, and the cars that stand in the daytime – have they the memories I once had? Let me walk past the gas-works, away from the car parks – I will climb Beacon Hill, that's what I will do.

The bank is steep and I am not as bloody young as I was, funny I think of death a lot more now-a-days. I suppose it's what all 'bums' feel when they become failures, they don't see any reason for living. 'Whoops-a-daisy,' the steps leading up Beacon Hill are chipped and broken, I'm gasping like an old codger, but I'll climb this bloody hill. The breeze is lovely, listen how it rustles through the lonesome bushes, well they are not lonesome really. Darkness is all around me, but there are still some lights on in the town, slipping, can't seem to keep a hold, but I will. Gripping tufts of grass, clay sticking to my shoes, I am determined to climb the hill, higher and higher, and it seems to make me cleaner and cleaner. I am enjoying myself now, like pretending to be a mountain climber when I was a kid, keep going and yer will get there!

Who speaks? — who is making the grunts and groans, as if another person was beside me? Oh I am so tired, yet it is a wonderful tiredness, I can feel the sweat trickle in my eyes, up and up I go, I am getting sober. The breeze has transformed into a whistling wind up it comes, through the silent bushes, passing me as it races up the hillside. Cruel and immodest in its rush to the top of the hill. You Bastard! You Bastard! I'll be up there with you, I shout, but I know he is ignorant of me. The lights are out in the town, but for the candle-like lights of the main street of the town centre. I am on the plateau (flat) of Beacon Hill and this is as far as I am going. Wish I could build a really tall house on this flat land, and look down on Woolshops and the gas-works and the copper works. Yes that is something I would really like, yes the solitude, but for the wind brushing the trees it would be heaven. I could watch the hustle and bustle of the town centre and smile at the 'rat race' below. If anyone wanted to visit me, let them climb the hill, ha! ha! ha! Well that would prove their friendship in this materialistic world.

Love that is what I really want mam! Not the violence and hatred that I have only known. But how does one go about showing people that you really can love. Is it truly possible that I could write down my feelings, my memories? Oh God! Mam, I feel such a feeling of love coming up inside me, what was it you said? So long ago when we both laid in the darkness of our bedroom? Yes I remember: "Well you won't lose will you love?" — they was the very words. You won't lose will you. I feel the excitement — the challenge standing looking down into the womb of Woolshops. I must shout, I won't bloody lose, I'll show the lot of you, the echo comes back from the Town and Woolshops like a soprano voice of someone I knew. Anyway, what did it matter, the town was sleeping.